THE EMPATHIC BRAIN

How the discovery of mirror neurons changes our understanding of human nature

CHRISTIAN KEYSERS

First Published June 2011 as a Kindle E-Book

Cover and book designed by Christian Keysers, in-text illustrations by Valeria Gazzola.

ISBN: 9789081829205

About The Cover: Le Baiser by Rodin is my favorite sculpture. The symmetry of two lovers' kiss is a metaphor for our brain's capacity to mirror people's actions, sensations and emotions. The fusion, in love, of two souls epitomizes the empathic brain – and marked the start of the most meaningful experience of my life.

Social Brain Press

To Julia

CONTENTS

Introduction:

Connecting People

The best day of my life started off with what you could call a failure. Even little details of that moment will stay in my head forever. On a Saturday in January of 2004, fresh snow covered the rugged edges of the Dolomites around that small town called Castelrotto, in Italy. Valeria and I sat in a tiny church in front of two Catholic ministers. "You may now exchange your vows," one of the ministers said. My heart started beating strongly.

The words I was going to say–I had prepared and rehearsed them over and over in my head–were ready to be spoken, but now that Valeria was looking into my eyes, in front of my best friends and family, a knot formed in my throat, and tears appeared in the corners of my eyes. My voice started, began a word—more like a fraction of a word–and then quickly broke. Everybody was waiting for me to say something, and the silence around me was getting louder and louder. So I started again, listening to myself from the outside, like a stranger.

And then something happened. Still struggling with words, I glanced at the people around us. Instead of the impatience I expected, I saw how a dear friend of mine in the first row had pulled a handkerchief from his pocket. I looked at my father, and I saw his face covered in tears. Even our photographer wasn't taking pictures anymore. The people around me seemed to be feeling, at least in part, what I was feeling. Noticing and realizing that helped me go on. I was still shaking, and it still took me what felt like minutes to control my voice well enough to say those lines. But I finally managed to say them (—and she said "yes").

I'm telling this story, not because of what happened to me, but because of what happened to the others in the room. We have all experienced moments like these; moments in which we find ourselves moved–not because of what happened to us, but because of what happened to someone else.

Emotions of other people can become part of us; they can become *our* emotions, almost as if what happens to others spills over to us. Experiencing this doesn't even take effort. We just do it, automatically, intuitively, and largely uncontrollably. That is to say, our brains do it. In fact, this feat of our brain, the emotional connection with others is, to a large extent, what makes us human. But how does our brain do that? Why should the emotions of others affect us so much? That is what this book is all about.

Of course, we do not share only happy moments. Other emotions work just as well, as you'll soon see. Occasionally, I'm invited to give a talk to explain my line of research. Sometimes, the invitation comes from a remote part of the world, and I find myself talking to an audience with a totally different cultural background. Still, everybody seems to understand intuitively the movie clip I start off with.

The clip is taken from one of the movies I liked so much when I was a kid, *Dr. No*, with Sean Connery as James Bond. Bond is lying in bed, white sheets covering his sleeping body. Suddenly, a tarantula the size of a hand emerges from under the sheets and crawls toward his head. Each of the spider's steps seems to create a little dimple on Bond's skin where the sharp claw takes hold. Awakened by the tingling sensation, Bond tenses. His ears fill with the rhythmic thumping of his heart. Little droplets of sweat begin forming on his face, and he scans the bed in search of an object he can use to brush the spider away.

Since I've seen the clip at least a hundred times, I don't look at it anymore. Instead, I watch the audience. I pick out a few people I can see well, and, looking at their faces and bodies, I don't have to ask what goes on in their mind. I can *see* it. And I can feel their discomfort. Actually, it's a mixture of discomfort and pleasure, because even though they see the spider and sense Sean Connery's tension, they all know that they are perfectly safe. And yet, just watching the scene, their heartbeats accelerate, they start sweating a little, their bodies become tense, and some even feel their arms start itching as if the spider's claws were brushing their own skin. We connect with James Bond and start feeling what he feels. But why? Why are we so moved by movies? Why, as we sit comfortably on our living room sofa, does the sight of a movie trigger physiological responses that would only be appropriate if we were in danger ourselves?

Of course, not every day is wedding day and, thank God, most of us are not regularly attacked by super-sized spiders. But don't be mistaken. Even in the routine of our everyday lives, connecting with others, understanding how they feel, is a capacity we would certainly not want to miss. Social life would simply break down without it.

Waking up in the morning, looking at my wife Valeria, my brain needs to instantly solve a number of complicated and, for my marriage, vitally important questions, such as: What is hiding behind her sleepy face? A wish for a hug because she just woke up from a bad dream? An unspoken plea for me to prepare breakfast? At work, I have to decide whether my Dean's mood is good enough to ask him for the sabbatical I need to write this book. Back at home, longing to collapse on the couch, I have to figure out whether Valeria's offer to cook is sincere, or whether she really wants me to do it instead. All throughout the day, the success of our relationships and careers depends on our capacity to read the emotions and states of others. Very often we do manage to sense the inner states of others even though they try to hide them. We feel sadness behind a faked smile, or bad intentions behind seemingly generous actions. How do we do it? How do we manage to feel what is concealed?

In the second half of the nineteenth Century, modern brain science began by asking basic questions about where language is located in the brain, how we memorize things, and how our brain moves our body. More than a hundred years later, in the 1980s and 1990s, emotions became more popular. Still, research was almost exclusively done on isolated individuals. The question of how we read the minds of others and are moved by their emotions remained largely untouched.

And with good reason. Scientists weren't studying the brain in social interactions because it's very hard to do. Testing complex human interactions is difficult by using animal models or observing a single person lying still in a brain scanner.

Another part of the reason it wasn't being studied was that, for a long time, nobody cared much about the question because it seemed trivial. Most children are experts at telling other people's emotions by age seven, and most of the time when we share the emotions of others, you're not even consciously *doing* anything; it just *happens* to you. You don't have to *think* to understand what Bond is going through when the spider crawls along his skin because you understand him intuitively. The task seemed so easy, so trivial in contrast to 'hard' things like calculus, which virtually no human can do before age sixteen, that we took this capacity for granted. Ironically, computers have been able do calculus since the 1950s, but recognizing that somebody next to you is happy or afraid turns out to be so difficult a task, that no modern computer or robot of the twenty-first century is able to do it. Why is understanding other people, which is so hard for computers, so much easier for us than something like calculus, which is so easy for computers?

If you think about it, understanding other people should indeed be very hard. The human brain is arguably the most complex organ in the known universe, and yet even children as young as seven feel that they can effortlessly determine what is going on in the minds–and hence the brains–of the people around them. If I threw some dice and asked you the outcome, you would say, "I can guess, but how could I know for sure?" Yet if you see a young man and a young woman rushing hand in hand into a bedroom at a party, giggling as they close the door, you could be almost certain of their inner states and could predict what was about to happen. Somehow, nature makes predicting the complex human brain paradoxically *easier* than predicting the result of a simple roll of the dice.

For a long time, we didn't have a clue about how the brain accomplishes this task, or how it became so good at figuring out what goes on in others. Then things started to change. At the beginning of the 1990's, colleagues of mine in Parma, Italy, discovered some special brain cells they coined "mirror neurons," which dramatically changed the way we look not only at the brain, but also our understanding of social interactions.

Mirror neurons "mirror" the behavior and emotions of the people surrounding us in such a way that the others become part of us. Knowing that such cells exist can explain many of the mysteries of human behavior. For instance, why it's so hard to stick to a diet if you see people around you that eat the very thing you should not. Mirror neurons provide an answer. When you grasp and eat a piece of chocolate, a certain network of brain cells, let's call it an "eat the chocolate network," is activated. Some of these cells are special. They become active not only when *you* eat the chocolate, but also when you see *another* person eat it. These cells are mirror neurons. As we will see in this book, these neurons make us share the experiences of others. Seeing other people eat chocolate triggers a feeling for what it would be like to do the same. That helps us understand what they do, but unfortunately, it also triggers a tendency to *do* the same. Mirror neurons make us fundamentally social —for better and worse.

Since the discovery of mirror neurons in the early 1990s, we have gained more and more insights into our social nature. Mirror neurons not only help us understand other people, they also provide surprising new responses to very old questions such as how evolution lead to human language and how our body is related to how we think.

Besides changing our view of human nature, studying mirror neurons also gives us insights into more inconspicuous aspects of our everyday lives, such as why your arms start twitching while you watch your favorite baseball player swings at a critical pitch, or why it's so hard for a pianist not to move his fingers while listening to a piece of piano music, or how we learn skills by simply watching what others do.

Since mirror neurons contribute to our connecting with other people, a dysfunction of these cells can lead to an "emotional disconnection" with others. Autistic people are emotionally cut off from the rest of us. Mirror neurons help us explore the source of this disconnection and inspire new therapies.

In addition, psychopaths such as Ted Bundy butcher people as if they don't care – mirror neurons help us understand why.

In this book, I will try to give new insights to these and other mysteries. Empathy is deeply engraved in the architecture of our brain. What happens to other people affects almost all areas of our brain. We were designed to be empathic, to connect with others. By unravelling the principles through which our brain makes us empathic, by discovering its elegant simplicity, I hope to share the awe and wonder that comes with finding out what makes us truly human.

1

The Discovery of Mirror Neurons

Vittorio is shaking his bearded head in disbelief. "Leo, non può essere!" (Leo, this can't be!). He grasps a raisin from the tray in front of the monkey. Out of the loudspeaker comes what seems to be the sound of a machine gun. It's not, of course. It's the sound of a single nerve cell "firing." A hair-thin electrode has been placed in the brain of the monkey and, as soon as the nerve cell is activated, the weak current measured through the electrode is amplified, transformed into sound by a loudspeaker and made visible by a green trace on the screen of an oscilloscope. "Are we picking up some noise? Can this be the same cell?" Looking at the oscilloscopes, Vittorio seems puzzled—everything looks perfectly normal—green spikes lighting up on a black background. Now the monkey grasps the raisin from the tray, and the response sounds and looks identical to when Vittorio took the raisin. "This is amazing!" Leo says.

When Vittorio retold me the events of that day, I was excited and amazed. But that warm August evening in the year 1990 at the University of Parma, Leonardo Fogassi, Vittorio Gallese, Giacomo Rizzolatti, and the rest of the team did not immediately realize what they had just discovered. Years later, the eminent neuroscientist Vilayanur Ramachandran would compare the revolutionary discovery the Italian scientists had, more or less accidentally, stumbled across, to the discovery of Jim Watson's and Francis Crick's double helix. "I predict that mirror neurons will do for psychology what DNA did for biology," he said

The team had discovered the first "mirror neuron," a very particular kind of brain cell. These cells are unique in that they respond not only when the monkey performs a particular action, such as grasping a small raisin, but also when the monkey sees someone else perform a similar action. Mirror neurons have radically changed our conception of how the brain works.

Before their discovery, accumulating knowledge about the basic function of many brain regions had created a vision of the brain that revolved around a strict division of labor (the most important of these regions, prevalent throughout this book, are illustrated in the section *Map of the Empathic Brain*). The cortex at the very back of the brain, called the primary visual cortex, was known to decompose the images from the retina in minute little details, focusing on edges and angles at particular places in the image. These details are then pieced together by brain areas in the temporal visual cortex (dark green in the diagram) where particular neurons respond to the unique combination of features that characterize a raisin and others to those that characterize your grandmother. More toward the front of the brain, brain regions that are called the premotor (PM and IFG on the diagram) and supplementary motor areas (SMA) had been discovered to start their activity *before* we perform a certain action. They seemed to program what we would be doing in the future. The primary motor cortex (M1) on the other hand activates when we actually move our body, and directly controls our muscles. All this knowledge had been combined in a vision of the brain that was pleasantly clear-cut. The brain had two halves. Perceiving the world or seeing a raisin, was done by the back half of the brain, while acting on the world, grasping the raisin, was performed by the front half of the brain (M1, PM, IFG and SMA).

The discovery of mirror neurons changed this view of the brain's division of labor. Mirror neurons have a dual purpose, both perceiving the world *and* acting on it. The nerve cell the group in Parma found was located in the premotor cortex (the area just in front of the primary motor cortex), where neurons were thought to deal only with programming the monkey's own actions. The neuron they found, though, was active both when the monkey grasped a raisin, which is not surprising for a premotor neuron, and also when the monkey saw someone else perform the same action, which was very surprising indeed, as responding to other people's actions was thought to be performed by a completely different area of the brain:

the temporal visual cortex. It was as if the brain of the monkey was pretending to do the action it was observing.

Finding a premotor neuron that responds to the sight of actions was as surprising as discovering that your television, which you thought just *displayed* images, had doubled all those years as a video camera that *recorded* everything you did. The simple dichotomy of input versus output function suddenly stopped making sense, and scientists got a first glimpse of the fact that in certain brain regions, doing and seeing may actually be the same.

At first, the team in Parma did not trust what they had discovered. After they recorded the first mirror neurons, the team suspected that the monkey simply happened to move while viewing the raisin being grasped. But careful observation of the monkey and recording of muscle activity revealed that the mirror neurons responded to the sight of grasping even in instances when the monkey was still. Slowly the team warmed up to the possibility that some premotor neurons—the mirror neurons—really did have a function that was detached from the monkey's overt behavior.

What, though, does it mean for a premotor neuron to fire while you are observing the actions of others? If premotor neurons are artificially stimulated, by injecting a small electrical current through the electrode normally used to record the neurons activity, the monkey stops what he is doing, and suddenly reaches out to grasp something[1]. Though this confirms that premotor neurons are indeed an integral part of the monkey's own actions, the question remains of what the monkey "feels" when this happens . Some of our own movements can feel involuntary. For example, if you sit on the edge of a table and tap the spot under your knee-cap with a little hammer, your lower leg starts kicking, but you feel as if the movement was independent of your own will. If, on the other hand, you willingly extend your leg, the same movement feels very different–you wanted to extend your leg, and the leg "obeyed" your will. What then, does the monkey feel, when an experimenter activates its premotor neurons? Does the grasping action feel as involuntary as our knee-jerk reflex, or does the monkey feel as if it wants to grasp?

We have been able to find out the answer to this question because electro-stimulation of particular brain areas in humans is sometimes performed in the context of surgical procedures. For example, some patients with epilepsy have so many epileptic seizures a day that they can no longer live a normal life. If medication fails to reduce the frequency of the episodes, patients often seek surgery. Epileptic episodes start in a circumscribed part of the brain, and then slowly spread to the rest, so if the site in which the episode originates can be ascertained, surgical removal of that part of the brain can dramatically reduce the frequency of the episodes or even cure the epilepsy altogether. The problem is that the tissue that is removed is associated with some capacity of the brain and removing it will alter that capacity. To avoid altering important brain capacities, neurosurgeons sometimes stimulate various parts of the brain in order to deduce their function. Then, together with the patient, the surgeon can decide to remove the brain region or not, depending on whether the patient is willing to sacrifice that capacity to reduce the epilepsy or not. Disrupting language regions or basic motor systems, for instance, may be so debilitating that most patients would prefer to remain epileptic.

When neurosurgeons stimulate the primary motor cortex just posterior to where mirror neurons are found, the body of the patient starts to move. The stimulation can be performed while the patient is awake, because the brain itself does not have pain sensors. If asked what they feel, patients report: "My hand twitched," as if the source of the movement was out of their control—just like a knee-jerk reflex. If surgeons stimulate the brain areas in front of the primary motor cortex (i.e. the premotor or supplementary motor areas), patients perform more complex actions, such as bending their arm or grasping something. If asked what went on in their minds while moving, patients say that they "felt the urge to do that"[2]. Sometimes patients even subjectively feel an arm moving, although physically it did not. In light of these findings, the activity of the mirror neurons in the premotor cortex of the monkey while observing the actions of humans may be best understood as an inner feeling of relating to the actions of others, a sharing of the wish to act, analogous to the urge reported by the human patients after electrical stimulation of the same brain region. To come back to our example, seeing someone else eat chocolate would thus trigger premotor mirror neurons that would be responsible for making us plan to eat chocolate, and we would feel an urge to do the same.

IS PERCEPTION LIKE A SANDWICH?

When Vittorio Gallese and his colleagues published their discovery in the late 1990s, I was still finishing my master's degree. Some years later, while doing research for my doctorate in the medieval Scottish town of St. Andrews, I attended a lecture in which Vittorio spoke about his discoveries. I was immediately fascinated. "Most people see the way we perceive and react to other people as a sandwich," Vittorio said. "The top and bottom layers are the visual system, which allows us to see other people, and the motor system, which allows us to execute adequate motor reactions. From the point of view of how we read the minds of other people they are necessary, but unexciting, like the bread in a sandwich," he said, smiling. "Most people believe that how we understand other people is not through the visual and motor systems, but through a special process that happens between seeing what other people do and reacting to them. Nobody knows where that special process occurs, but it is considered the juiciest part of the problem–like the filling of the sandwich."

Vittorio was right. In the 1990s, neuroscience had begun to understand the mechanisms of visual processing that allow our brain to build a representation of what it sees in the world. The problem is that *seeing* what is in the world is not the same as *understanding* the world. For instance, if I see you grasp a piece of chocolate, bring it to your mouth, and smile, I understand both that you ate chocolate and that you are satisfied. I intuitively understand what you are feeling in addition to simply *seeing* what you do. In the 1990s, what we knew was that there were neurons in the visual cortex that responded to the sight of someone bringing an object to his mouth. They fire if, and only if, someone brings an object to the mouth. But the visual system itself knows nothing about what eating chocolate really means: the delicious sweet and bitter taste in your mouth, the creamy consistency, the longing it can trigger, the delightful aftertaste . . .

The motor system, on the other hand, was thought to deal with the elaborate programming of actions. If you saw someone eat chocolate and went ahead and did the same, the motor system was thought to be involved only in the action of doing the same, *after* you had seen the other person eat, *after* you had analyzed and recognized what the other person had done, and *after* you had decided for yourself that you wanted a piece, too. The motor system was a sheer executor of cognitive processes occurring elsewhere. Clearly, the most interesting bit in terms of understanding others must be a process that occurs after you have seen what another person has done but before you take an appropriate action. The most popular belief in the 1990s was that there was a specialized part of the brain that "mentalized," or thought about, other people's inner life based on the input from the visual system. The system could propose appropriate reactions, and then the motor/premotor cortex would take over and implement those actions. Many scientists were hunting for this "mentalizing module."

The study of autism was thought to be the key to understanding this mentalizing process. Autistic individuals appear to have normal visual systems (having little trouble describing what the world around them looks like), and normal motor systems (performing most motor tasks as well as comparable non-autistic people). Their mentalizing processes, though, seem different from those of most other individuals. If I show you a bag of M&Ms and ask you what is inside, you would say, "M&Ms." If I open the bag to reveal that it really contains coins, you would be surprised. If your friend then enters the room, and I ask you, "What will your friend answer if I ask him what's in the bag?" you would answer, "Well, M&Ms."

In France, my friend and colleague Bruno Wicker has performed a similar test on autistic patients, including, when I went to visit him, a young man by the name of Jerome. "He is just finishing his PhD in theoretical physics. A really smart guy!" said Bruno as we were waiting.

When Bruno introduced me, Jerome looked around the room, but never into my eyes. The tone of his voice as he said hello was flat, almost mechanical. "We would like to ask you something," Bruno said, pulling a box of Danish cookies from his desk. "What do you think is in this box?" he asked. "Cookies," Jerome answered. Bruno opened the box to reveal a set of colored pencils instead of the expected cookies. "Ah," said Jerome. Bruno closed the box as his research assistant entered the room. "What do you think she would think the box contains?" Bruno asked Jerome. The question seemed insultingly trivial to me. "Jerome studies theoretical physics for heaven's sake," I almost wanted to say. Jerome, though, did not seem insulted. "Colored pencils," he replied. I was stunned. Although complex mathematical equations were crystal clear to him, his capacity to understand what other people knew or didn't know was impaired. Fascinated by observations like these, an increasing number of researchers in the late 1990s began hunting for a specialized part of the brain that dealt with understanding the minds of others—the juicy filling in the sandwich that Vittorio was talking about.

FROM SEEING TO DOING

"What mirror neurons tell us," Vittorio said in his lecture, "is that these mentalizing processes are not the only juicy bit. The very motor processes through which we react to other people's actions–the boring bread in the classic sandwich–are where the most exciting process of all appears to occur: your actions become my actions. I feel what you do. Somehow understanding the actions of others does not always require mentalizing. Mirror neurons in your premotor cortex, in this very pragmatic area, appear to give us an intuitive understanding of the actions of other people."

As I went to eat my lunch that day, my sandwich somehow had a very different taste. I realized that Vittorio and his team had found a key to solving the biggest riddle of social interactions, that is, why it is so easy for humans to know what is going on in other people's minds. This seemingly philosophical question is very old, but hundreds of years of investigations had focused on explicit, logical solutions that failed to provide a satisfying answer. Now, neuroscience had discovered a phenomenon that shed a new light on the debate; meaning is added to what the visual system detects by linking it to our own actions. Once I link the sight of someone grasping a piece of chocolate and bringing it to his mouth with my own ability to do so, what I see stops being an abstract impression, devoid of meaning. The knowledge of how to eat chocolate is linked with the image of the action, thereby adding a very pragmatic meaning to what the visual system detects. If I show you a new sailing knot and ask you, "Understood?", you tying the knot in front of me would be the most convincing evidence that you had understood my demonstration. Mirror neurons, by linking the sight of an action with the motor program involved in executing the same action do exactly that by transforming what you see into how to do it.

I was so fascinated by this discovery that I applied for a fellowship to work with the team in Parma, and arrived there a year later, two weeks after handing in the final version of my PhD thesis in the fall of 2000, with a car full of boxes and a head full of ideas.

I drove my old VW Golf and the trailer that had barely survived the long drive from Scotland to Emgland, the Ferry, Belgium, Germany and Switzerland to a new building just outside the center of Parma, next to the city's large hospital. The three-story modern building had recently replaced the old structure in which the first mirror neurons had been discovered a decade earlier. Vittorio showed me around, offered me a coffee from the little espresso machine that was the center of the social life at the institute, and ten minutes later we were in the lab.

The first thing I heard was the sound of machine gun fire. Then I saw two researchers, Alessandra Umiltà and Evelyne Kohler, ripping sheets of paper in front of a monkey. I couldn't resist the temptation—I had to test my first mirror neuron. I watched as a monkey picked up a peanut, hearing the activity of the neuron through the amplifier. I then grabbed a peanut myself, and the monkey's neuron fired again. I was amazed. Alessandra smiled at me. "Experiencing a mirror neuron first hand is a lot more convincing than reading about them in papers, isn't it?" I tried picking up the peanut again, but this time with my other hand and from a very different angle, and yet the neuron fired again, as if to tell me, "I don't care how you grasp. I'm not stupid: I see you grasp and therefore I fire!"

BRAIN FUNCTION BASED ON CONNECTIONS BETWEEN NEURONS

To understand mirror neurons, it is essential to understand how neurons work more generally, and how the brain uses multiple neurons to achieve a certain capacity. Neurons in the brain are little processing units working in a processing chain. They receive inputs from neurons that precede them and send outputs to neurons that come after them. These inputs and outputs are of a chemical nature. A

A neuron releases small doses of neurotransmitters, chemicals that transmit messages between neurons, from its nerve endings, which are called synapses. These chemicals flow to the next neuron in the chain. If just a single dose of neurotransmitter is released onto the next neuron, not much happens. If the sending neuron however is very active, it will send multiple doses, and/or if other neurons join in and release their own burst of neurotransmitters, these inputs add up. When the sum of these doses gets above the threshold of the downstream neuron, the neuron triggers a brief pulse of electrical activity called an "action potential," which has two effects. First, it leads to the release of neurotransmitters from the synapses of this neuron, which now becomes a sending neuron. Second, the action potential is such a strong electrical event that it can be picked if a small electrode is inserted into the brain in the vicinity of that neuron. Once amplified and sent to a loudspeaker, it creates the "pop" sound we hear in our laboratory. The more input a cell receives, the more often it gets pushed over the action threshold, and the more frequent these pops, thus creating the characteristic sound of rapid gunfire that indicates that a neuron is very active. By listening to the amplified sound, we can know how active a neuron is and get a sense of the activity of that particular stage of the processing chain.

In addition to the excitatory synapses that augment the activity of a cell, other synapses, called inhibitory synapses, have the opposite effect, and reduce the activity of the receiving nerve cell.

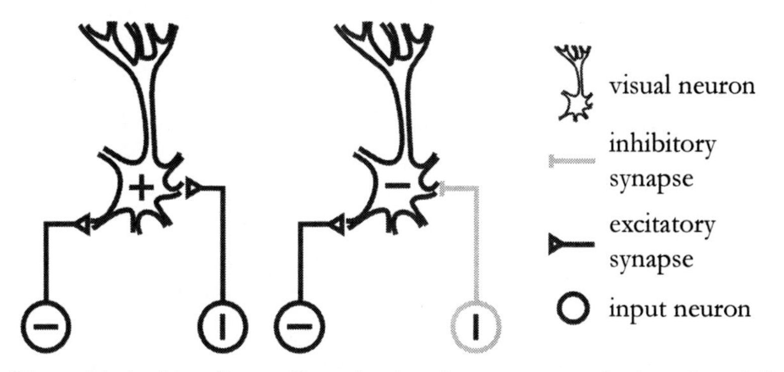

Figure 1.1: A wiring diagram illustrating how the same neuron (top) can be a "+" detector if it receives excitatory input from two visual neurons responding to hori-zontal and vertical bars, or a "-" detector if it receives excitatory input from the for-mer and inhibitory input from the latter.

The brain contains about one hundred billion neurons (i.e., a 1 with 11 zeros behind it) connected by 10^{15} synapses and it is the pattern of these connections that determines the function of the nervous system (see Figure 1.1). If a neuron receives an excitatory input from a neuron responding to a vertical bar and another excitatory input from a neuron responding to a horizontal bar, it will fire most whenever it sees a plus sign. If a similar neuron were to receive an excitatory inputs from the neuron responding to horizontal bars but an inhibitory input from the neuron responding to a vertical bar, it would no longer respond to a plus sign, but to a minus sign. The important factor is that the plus detector cell is not different from the minus detector in and by itself, but because of its pattern of connection with other neurons.

The physiologists David Hubel and Torsten Wiesel were the first to implant wires capable of recording from single neurons into the brain of a monkey. They found exactly the type of detectors described above in the occipital cortex, located at the back of the head. When they implanted the electrodes, though, they did not know what kind of connections the neuron there happened to have and what stimulus to use to increase their activity. A bit of detective work was needed, because the amount of stimuli that can be tried on a particular cell is enormous. A cell could respond most strongly to sight, sound, touch, smell, taste, or movement, or some combination thereof. A particular neuron may respond to the taste of sugar, but you may spend all day comparing vertical and horizontal bars without getting any closer to discovering that a sweet taste is the stimulus that works best for that neuron.

The impossibility to test all possible stimuli is why it took so long to discover mirror neurons. They are located in the premotor cortex, where almost all neurons respond while the monkey performs particular actions, such as grasping a raisin. Nobody thought of standing in front of the monkey to see if the neurons also responded to a completely different class of stimuli, the *sight* of someone else grasping a raisin. Imagine you were searching for wine in a supermarket, glanced down an aisle, and saw that all the shelves contained beer bottles. You probably wouldn't start looking behind the beers to check whether the wine might be hidden there.

While grasping a raisin to hand it to the monkey in order to test if a particular neuron responded when the monkey grasped a small object, the team in Parma accidentally noticed that the neuron also fired while the *experimenter* took the raisin. At first, one ignores such additional activations, because they do not fit the image we have of that brain area's function – just as we would overlook the wine bottle in the beer aisle. What is more, 90 percent of the cells in this region indeed do not respond to the sight of other individuals' actions. But after this activity occurred over and over again, the team in Parma started to take their observation seriously. In a way, it was sheer luck that brought the team to notice the existence of mirror neurons, but insight allowed them to recognize the significance of their finding.

THE BRAIN VOCABULARY OF ACTION

Almost all neurons in the premotor cortex are involved in performing a specific action, but the selectivity of the neurons varies. The "selectivity" of a neuron reflects how much a neuron responds to each possible stimulus. To draw an analogy, I could measure your selectivity for music by playing you various pieces of pop, rock, jazz and classical music. If you respond positively to classical, but not to all other types of music, I would say that you are very selective, and that you are selective for classical music. Somebody else might respond positively only to jazz, and not at all to any other kind of music including classical music. That person would also be selective, but for jazz. Yet another person might moderately respond to all of the music I played, and that person would be less selective.

The same is true for nerve cells. Some respond strongly only while the monkey takes an object between its index finger and thumb but not at all to any other action, others respond only while the monkey takes an object by wrapping all his fingers around it but not to any other action, others still would respond to both forms of prehension and also when he takes the object with his lips.

Through their differing selectivity, neurons represent a "vocabulary" of actions that can be combined into larger units of actions. The action sequence "eating peanuts," for instance, can be created by combining different neurons: first neurons selectively active during the shell breaking, then those for picking the peanut out of the shell, then those bringing it to the mouth, and so on. Thus, the sequence of activity in these cells with different selectivities creates a complex action. The neurons resemble words, and the sequence of neural activation, phrases. A particular set of premotor neurons can be used to compose different sequences of actions. For instance, Many of the neurons involved in the peanut eating example can also be used to eat raisins, although the shell-breaking neurons would be omitted. In a way, the activity of premotor neurons reflects the language of action. And in this verbal analogy, more or less selective neurons correspond to words with different specificity. The most selective cells correspond to very specific verbs such as "picking-with-your-fingertips," the less selective ones would be more akin to the verb "taking," which does not specify how you do it.

BRINGING VISIONS INTO THE WORLD OF MOVEMENT

Only about 10 percent of the premotor neurons are the mirror neurons that respond when the monkey sits still and watches the actions of others. There is no way of knowing if a neuron is a mirror neuron or a regular premotor neuron while the monkey himself performs an action. At present, we have no reason to believe that these mirror neurons are shaped differently from other neurons. More likely, they differ from the other neurons only because of their connections.

Mirror neurons somehow receive excitatory inputs from visual regions of the brain that respond to the sight of other people's actions. Through these connections, they "translate" the visual language into the motor language of the monkey's own actions.

If we think about it, this translation is quite a miracle. Let's imagine the photograph of a sheep and the sound of the word "sheep" in our ears. These two things are fundamentally different, and yet our brain associates them together so strongly that we actively have to think to realize that they have nothing obvious in common, and that a French speaker, for instance, would fail to recognize that they belong together. Somehow our brain translates the sound of the word into an image of what the animal looks like, and vice versa.

The same is true for our actions. While we execute an action, our brain causes our muscles to move. Seeing the actions of someone else, on the other hand, involves light hitting our eyes. These are again two fundamentally different things. And yet our brain associates them so intensely that we almost find it hard to realize that, physically, there is nothing in common between muscles moving in our body and light hitting our retina. If mirror neurons respond both while the monkey performs certain actions and while he perceives others doing the same actions, the pattern of neural connections between the visual cortex and the mirror neurons must have translated the visual language of seeing other people into the motor language of doing actions.

HOW THE BRAIN ENCODES GOALS

Mirror neurons differ in the precision with which they translate observed actions into executed actions. *Broadly congruent* mirror neurons translate the actions of other individuals in fairly general terms. They often have relatively broad motor selectivity, responding, for instance, when the monkey grasps a peanut whether with his hand or with his mouth. Likewise, they respond to the sight of grasping in a variety of cases, and translate it into very general terms, such as "taking" or "grasping." Such a transformation is remarkable because someone grasping with his hand or with his mouth looks very different, and yet these different visual descriptions are translated into a single word of the motor language of premotor neurons, "taking." Some broadly congruent mirror neurons are quite specific when the monkey takes an action himself, for instance responding only when he takes an object between his thumb and index finger of the right hand. Yet it will respond whenever the monkey sees someone else grasp, irrespective of whether it is done with the hand or the mouth.

Although for these mirror neurons the correspondence between observed and executed actions is rather broad (hence their name), at a conceptual level of "taking" or "grasping in general," other mirror neurons are much stricter. Some are active only while the monkey grasps with the right hand, and also respond only while watching someoneelse grasp with the right hand. Others respond only to grasping with the mouth. Others, still more selective, respond while the monkey performs a precision grip, but not if the object is taken using the whole hand, and also only while a precision grip is being observed. These more selective neurons are called *strictly congruent* mirror neurons.

Such a multilevel design may appear redundant and unnecessary. If the details are correctly translated by strictly congruent mirror neurons, why have neurons that are as unspecific as "taking"? The answer might be simple. Imagine you are attending a tango class and have to understand how to perform the *gancho* (i.e., leg flip) that your instructor is demonstrating. Having never done a *gancho* before, you lack the precise motor program for *ganchos*, and hence have no strictly congruent mirror neurons for this skill. You do lift your leg every time you walk though, and broadly congruent mirror neurons for this action will become active during the observation of a *gancho*, giving you at least the broad sense that you need to lift your foot backwards. The broadly congruent mirror neurons might thus be particularly important for new actions, the details of which you have never performed. Through training, you can then refine your own *gancho* starting from a leg lift. As you become a more experienced tango dancer, your instructor may want you to perform very specific *ganchos* in a specific sequence. Once you will have acquired motor programs for different types of *ganchos* you will have different strictly congruent mirror neurons for each of these subtypes of *ganchos* that will respond only and selectively to the sight and execution of a particular *gancho*, enabling you to imitate such a specific sequence.

With the simultaneous multilevel translation implemented by the mix of broadly and strictly congruent mirror neurons, the monkey is equipped with a very flexible translation that resembles the zoom lens of a camera, able to zoom in on the details of the actions of other individuals, if in the monkey's motor vocabulary, or zoom out to get a more general sense of the scene.

WHAT HAPPENS WHEN WE HEAR AN ACTION?

So far, I've been writing about the sight of other individuals' actions. Often, though, we can understand the actions of other people simply by listening to them. In the 1980s, Coca-Cola had a famous radio commercial that featured the sound of a bottle opening with a hiss of pressure, a metal lid hitting the table and vibrating, liquid pouring into a glass, the "glug-glug" of eager swallowing, and finally, the satisfied "ah!" of a refreshed drinker. Now, twenty years later, I can still feel my mouth water at these sounds on a hot day. Why does the sound of the actions of others have such an irresistibly strong impact on our own body?

We discovered the answer shortly after I arrived in Parma. Vittorio, Alessandra and Evelyne had recorded from mirror neurons that appeared to respond not just when the monkey saw and did certain actions, but also when the monkey heard the sounds of these actions. We wanted to understand how well such neurons could differentiate between different actions, and how well their visual and auditory responses corresponded. Clearly, if such neurons are to help us understand the actions of others, they have to translate you ripping a sheet of paper into me ripping one, and you drinking a glass of soda into me drinking one. What we do not want, is your ripping action to also trigger my drinking or your drinking, my ripping – otherwise, how would you feel whether I was drinking or ripping?

First, we recorded from a neuron that responded when the monkey ripped a sheet of paper. I then soaked the paper in water to make ripping silent, covered the monkey's eyes, and gave him the paper, which he quickly ripped. Despite the monkey's inability to see or hear, the same cell fired, indicating that it was truly a motor neuron for ripping paper. The same neuron did not fire when the monkey broke a peanut, demonstrating selectivity. To then test the neuron's response to actions the monkey could only hear,we stood behind the monkey and loudly ripped a dry sheet of paper. The neuron still fired, as if the monkey had just ripped a sheet of paper himself. We broke the shell of a peanut behind the monkey, and nothing happened, suggesting that the cell involved in listening showed a similar selectivity for paper ripping over peanut breaking. . For a final test, we soaked some more paper, stood in front of the monkey and silently ripped the wet sheet of paper. Again, the neuron fired. However, when we broke a peanut, which we had ruptured before to make the motion silent, the neuron remained inactive.

What this finding means is that mirror neurons appear to combine the sight, the sound and the execution of an action. They are "trilingual." The most important finding, however, was that mirror neurons are selective in all three modalities. After finding many more neurons like this one, it became clear to me that radio advertisements like that of Coca-Cola make us long for a product because auditory mirror neurons selectively activate the motor programs we associate with consuming and enjoying these products.

2

The Power of Intuition

Paradoxically, the major hurdle to understanding the human mind is the obsession for rationality of the minds of the scientists that study it. The second hurdle is computers. Together, they have created the vision of a brain that processes all information in a conscious, logical and abstract way–much as ordinary computers do. The discovery of mirror neurons changed this vision.

If I had asked my grandmother how she knew I was in love, she would have told me that she just "felt" it. She knew that the processes through which we understand other people are not logical but intuitive. If you had asked many scientists in the 1980s, they would have told you something about observable facts (e.g., daydreaming, smiling etc.) combined with a theory of what "love" is (e.g., love includes daydreaming and happiness), as if intuition was irrelevant.

The difference in their responses reflects a systematic problem: the scientists that build our understanding of the brain become good scientists because they enjoy rational empirical thinking, and as such, they are inclined to believe that rational thinking is a more valuable process than intuition. Accordingly, before the discovery of mirror neurons, our vision of brain functioning in general, and of social understanding in particular, was dominated by the idea that our brain understands the world as a scientist would, by collecting evidence and rationally deriving a theory of the world based on this empirical evidence.

The scientists' abstract rational vision was further cemented into the minds of people through the trap of what you could call the "brain-computer-fallacy." Brains, like most biological things, are hard to understand because we did not build them. Computers on the other hand are easy to understand, at least for the engineers that make them. As computers became widely available in the 1970s and 1980s, a lot of computer engineers looked at brain science for ideas on how to make good computers. This is fine, but brain scientists have also looked at computers for hints about how the human mind could be working. The idea is that if a computer behaves like we do, whatever it is that makes the computer "intelligent" must give us clues to what makes us intelligent.

Of course, comparing our brains to computers is a fallacy. Both leopards and Ferrari's are fast, but should we therefore assume that a combustion engine must be hidden somewhere in the leopard? Unfortunately, many cognitive scientists have more or less consciously fallen into a similarly wrong line of thinking. The great American artificial intelligence pioneer, Doug Lenat, for instance, designed a computer program meant to approximate human thinking. Lenat's team fed the program millions of items of encyclopedic (hence the shortened name "Cyc") knowledge, much of which was similarly structured knowledge about the non-social world (e.g., "all cars are machines" and "all machines eventually stop working") and the human world ("all humans are animals" and "all animals get tired eventually"). If you ask this "Cyc" whether your car can be driven forever, it will deduce that because your car is a machine and all machines stop working, so will your car, and the answer is thus "no." If you ask it whether *you* can run forever, it will use the same line of thought to conclude that you will eventually get tired and stop running. By itself, "Cyc" is a great success. Its knowledge helps it browse the internet and provide relevant answers to many questions. Unfortunately though, the success of such expert programs has been taken as evidence that the rational abstract thinking used by "Cyc" is a viable explanation of how our brain works.

As we will see, mirror neurons, however, show us that abstract thinking is not the only process we use while observing the behavior of other organisms. Ironically, it might be that our grandmothers' intuitive answer "because I felt it" captures our nature better than to most rational scientists' vision of the mind as a logical, disembodied information processing computer.

WE PREDICT THE ACTIONS OF OTHERS BASED ON WHAT WE WOULD DO

How does a monkey predict the actions of other monkeys or humans? Does it use abstract rules? The answer is probably no. As we have seen, when the monkey witnesses the actions of other individuals, some premotor neurons that would normally be activated while performing the same action, are activated.

During the monkey's own behavior, reaching toward a peanut is usually followed by grasping. In the wiring structure of the premotor neurons, activity thus routinely spreads from reaching neurons to grasping neurons. The observation of reaching, transformed into premotor activity by mirror neurons, will then have the same structure of connections and therefore spread to grasping neurons. These would thus become active before the grasping itself could be observed, enabling the prediction of the behavior of others based on the rules that govern the monkey's own behavior.

To test whether this type of prediction occurs in the mirror neuron system, we recorded from a mirror neuron that responded when the monkey grasped an orange. A member of the team then grasped an orange in front of the monkey and the same mirror neuron fired at the moment when the orange was seen to be grasped. This of course is what mirror neurons do. In cases when the orange was taken away and the experimenter just reached toward the location where it had been, the neuron typically remained silent, indicating that the neuron really coded grasping an object and not just opening and closing the hand. The critical test of prediction followed. An opaque screen was placed in front of the orange so that all the monkey saw was a hand reaching toward and disappearing behind the screen. Half of the mirror neurons fired in the hidden case, as if they could deduce from the sight of the reaching movement that the hand was going to grasp the orange because that is what the monkey would normally do himself[3].

Understandably, such predictions could be very useful. If a monkey sees a leopard run toward him and disappear from sight behind a bush, being able to predict the grasping with the mouth action that is going to follow will give the monkey time to jump up a tree. In less dramatic cases, a monkey may have found a nice fruit. Seeing a fellow monkey reach toward it can mean losing that juicy treat, unless the behavior is predicted and the fruit moved away. In the complex environment in which monkeys live, being better at predicting the behavior of others can mean having more time to respond to the upcoming but foreseen situation.

The monkey's method differs fundamentally from the way a computer would predict behavior. Computers don't grasp for or eat fruit; therefore they cannot use their own behavior to predict that of animals. Monkeys, on the other hand, routinely perform most of the actions other monkeys might. They can map the behavior of their fellows onto their own body and actions. The prediction is no longer based on a set of propositional rules specifically acquired to predict the behavior of other individuals, but uses the machinery that governs the observer's own actions and body to run a simulation of what the observer would do next, and the predicted behavior is then attributed to the observed animal The classical divide between self and other and between body and mind becomes fuzzy and permeable in this process. The *mind*-function of predicting another's behavior is now based on the neural representation of the observer's own *body* and actions, it becomes "embodied," i.e., founded and grounded in the body[i]. The other organism is thus represented in parts of the brain of the observer that were thought to be dedicated to dealing with the monkey's self.

Using the self as a simulation of other individuals is a very economical and elegant form of computation, because instead of requiring an explicit set of rules about others, it utilizes the machinery that specializes in *doing* ones own actions to also *predict* the actions of others. The discovery that the brain actually uses this form of embodied simulation changes our view of the brain. For the first time, social cognition is no longer just any old form of computation but a very specific one that relies on the resemblances between organisms. In now makes sens why we find it so much easier to predict the behavior of the giggling couple tiptoeing toward the bedroom at a party than that of dice–because we are people, not dice.

UNDERSTANDING OTHERS: WHAT IT WOULD FEEL LIKE TO DO THE SAME

As we have seen earlier, stimulation of premotor neurons in humans does not just mechanically move the body; it also creates mental states associated with actions, such as the feeling that our own arm is moving, even when it is not, or a sense of wanting to do something ('I feel an urge to do something with my hand'[2]). The activations measured in this area while monkeys observe the actions of others could thus generate a conscious "feeling" for the observed actions, an inner sense for these actions akin to the wish to act induced by stimulation of the brain. Considering the selectivity of neurons in the premotor cortex for particular actions, often independent of the precise way in which the actions are performed (i.e., grasping with the right or left hand, or even with the mouth), we can also get an idea of what aspects of the action are represented in the premotor activations, which turns out to be the goal of the action, and not so much what muscles were moved. To take an example, if the monkey sees you take an orange with your left arm, the premotor activity would primarily provide the monkey with the feeling that you are taking the orange, and not so much a detailed sequence of how you contract your triceps, extend your fingers, flex your finger, contract your biceps and so on. As such, the premotor cells are not just detailed predictors of the behavior to come, but also convey a feeling for their goal, or intention, and thereby get a bit closer to what we would call "understanding the intentions of others."

The word intention here is meant in a very down-to-earth sense meaning what the agent tries to achieve. Whether monkeys have such intentions is hard to know, but their behavior is compatible with the idea that they do. I remember handing a marshmallow to Florence, one of my monkeys. She liked marshmallows, and her hand swiftly reached out toward it. When I playfully retracted the mallow, she jerked her head forward with an angry expression. For humans such anger goes hand in hand with a feeling that someone is playing with one's intentions, which leads me–through simulation in my own mind–to believe that monkeys do have a sense of intention that resembles mine.

The word "understanding" is likewise meant in a very pragmatic way. The monkey may "feel" the observed action (e.g., the hand grasping the orange behind the screen), much like patients with electrostimulation in higher motor areas feel their arm moving. This does not mean that the monkey understands the whole depth of our intentions (*why* we want to grasp the orange), but it shows that understanding goals and predicting actions are tightly linked phenomena, and that mirror neurons may give a sense of the immediate aim of an observed action (e.g., getting the orange).

In itself, even this pragmatic form of understanding intention is a small miracle. My wish to get the orange is hidden inside my head, but through observing my behavior, the monkey senses my hidden internal intentions. With mirror neurons, monkeys become virtually "telepathic." Again, instead of postulating a rich set of propositional rules that allow us to deduce intentions from behavior, the brain of the monkey maps the behavior of other individuals onto its own, thereby activating a sense of the observed actions through an embodied simulation that relies more on the machinery of motor control than abstract thinking.

The new perspective provided by the above paradigm gets much closer to our life experience, where we do not have to think all the time while watching a James Bond movie, but instead our body just seems to tense when Bond is tense, and we feel what Bond is feeling. Of course, abstract thinking can add importantly to such embodied simulation by allowing us to include knowledge about secret agents (for which we lack first person experience) into our reflections, but this thinking is not the only way through which we appear to gain insights into other individuals. The preconscious embodied simulation that mirror neurons perform may be fundamental for our social intuition.

HOW MIRROR NEURONS FACILITATE IMITATION

When I heard Vittorio first speak about mirror neurons, I thought that such neurons must be the basis of our capacity for learning how to do things by watching someone else. The School of Psychology in the University of St. Andrews where I was doing my PhD at that time has two of the world's most famous experts in the study of primate cognitive and social capacities, Andy Whiten and Dick Byrne. Through talking with them, I was aware of cases in which monkeys and apes learn skills from watching each other.

A famous example is potato washing. If a young monkey finds a potato in the soil, it could of course start eating it, but the grinding of sand between its teeth would be an unpleasant sensation. In Japan, monkeys have been observed to wash their potatoes in salt water in a simple procedure that removes the soil from them, and adds salt that, as we all know, gives potatoes a more palatable taste. Interestingly, these Japanese monkeys are the only group of monkeys known to wash potatoes, and infant monkeys have to learn how to wash the potatoes from the adults. The washing has become a local tradition, and is often taken as an example of culture, that is, the transmission of knowledge in a society. Given the importance of culture for our own species, the transmission of culture in monkeys has received much interest, with the question of how student monkeys can learn from their teachers being central.

Hearing about mirror neurons, one might think, "Well it's easy. Seeing someone else wash potatoes activates washing mirror neurons, and the student starts washing his own potatoes in imitation." That is what I thought as well. But every primatologist told me that monkeys may have mirror neurons, and they do learn by observation, but they do not imitate in the strictest sense. I was surprised, but they told me that strict imitation is not just learning from observation, but being able to copy the exact movements that the demonstrator used to perform the action. Monkeys learn to achieve goals they observe, but they tend to develop their own way of achieving them. The distinction between strict imitation and learning to achieve a goal puzzled me for years, and I only really began to understand it much later, after a number of studies we performed in humans.

3

Human Mirroring

Valeria and I met in Parma, on a rock-climbing course. She was finishing her studies in biology, and I was working on mirror neurons in monkeys. Our relationship moved slowly after that first meeting. We met from time to time in group settings, but it took a trip with just the two of us to a conference in San Francisco to make it clear that our future was together. We returned to Italy after the trip to San Francisco and quickly moved in together. Two years later, we married, and then, in 2004 we moved to Groningen, the Netherlands to begin an exciting new venture together of opening our own neuroscience laboratory in the newly created Neuro*I*maging Center where we would study the mirror neuron system in humans. But while we had been busy with wedding plans, starting a new life, and getting our lab set up, research into mirror neurons continued in leaps and bounds, providing the underpinnings of our own research.

Seeing an action activates our body

Shortly after the team in Parma first discovered mirror neurons in monkeys, neuroscientists interested in the social mind everywhere in the world began to debate whether a similar system exists in humans. Unfortunately, it is more difficult to investigate their existence because we can't often directly measure mirror neurons in humans. At present, the only way to record the activity of single neurons is to implant thin wires into the brain, as we have done in monkeys. Clearly, implanting such thin wires has risks. They can damage the brain tissue slightly, just like the thin hypodermic needles used to inject insulin slightly damage the skin they go through. Unlike skin, the brain is very bad at repairing itself. A prick to the skin quickly heals but a stroke in the brain, as we know all too well, often has permanent consequences. Implanted wires can also serve as an entry route for infections, and infections in the brain are particularly hard to fight. Implanting such wires in humans for the sake of investigating mirror neurons alone is thus clearly not justifiable.

We therefore had to base our understanding of the human mirror system mainly on a combination of what we know about the mirror system in monkeys and the use of non-invasive methods. Brain scanning in particular is often used to provide convergent evidence of mirror neurons in humans. Rather than to make an exhaustive list of all the evidence we have for a mirror system in humans, I will present two examples that illustrate how the auditory mirror system can be studied in humans[ii].

MAGNETIZING THE MIRROR SYSTEM

LosAngeles, 2002, Ahmanson Lovelace Brain Mapping Center, UCLA: As Lisa Aziz-Zadeh later described me, she stands beside Peter, who is comfortably seated in a chair with a head rest. Wires run from his hands toward a computer next door. They are attached to little circular stick-on electrodes placed on the muscle between the thumb and index finger, and measure the activity in this muscle. "Try to relax," Lisa tells him, but her smile shows that she knows that it is not easy to relax in a lab, with her holding an alien-looking, butterfly-shaped device just over his head.

The "butterfly" is a coil through which a sudden current can be sent, creating a focused transient magnetic field that stimulates the brain. "Tock!" A little mechanical sound comes from the coil, indicating that the magnetic field has just been applied. Nothing happens. The computer screen, measuring the muscle activity from Peter's hand, shows a flat line. Lisa moves the coil backwards. "Tock!" Now one of Peter's fingers twitches and the line on the computer spikes slightly. Lisa attaches the coil to a holder. "Okay, now just listen carefully to the sounds," she says and goes out of the room, closing the door behind her.

The experiment begins. Sounds of footsteps come out of a loudspeaker, then sounds of an old-fashioned typewriter, then a thunderstorm, the typewriter again, and so on. Each sound is accompanied by the characteristic "tock" of the transcranial magnetic stimulation (TMS) machine sending its magnetic pulse.

After the participant has gone home, Lisa analyses the traces the computer recorded. When the participant listened to footsteps or thunderstorms, the line on the screen showed the same small spike it showed during the sound of thunder. On the trials where the participant heard the sound of typewriting, however, the exact same TMS pulse led to a *bigger* spike, and the finger moved more. Interestingly, this only worked when the coil was placed on the left side of the participant's head, over the finger area of the premotor cortex, not on the right side[8].

If we, like monkeys, have mirror neurons for sounds, we would expect that hearing the sound of hand actions should activate premotor neurons for hand actions that send connections to the primary motor hand action area. Without the TMS machine, hearing the sound of hand actions is not enough to make our hands start moving. The TMS pulse alone produced only a small twitch in the finger. But when the sound and the pulse came together, the twitch of the fingers was measurably larger. The experiment shows that the sound of hand actions does reach the muscles we would use to do the same action – only a little help, in form of a TMS pulse, is required to make this effect measurable.

At our institute in Parma, Luciano Fadiga had conducted a similar experiment years before, testing the visual system. He used TMS to stimulate the region of the primary motor cortex that led to finger movements. Participants watched movies of hand actions, as well as control stimuli such as images of objects. Results indicated that when participants saw hand movements, the TMS pulse lead to stronger twitches in the fingers.

These TMS experiments showed that the sight and sounds of other people's actions converged onto the observer's own motor programs, just as mirror neurons would predict. But where in the brain do they converge?

FROM PARMA TO HOLLAND: A DAY IN THE NEW LAB

Spring 2004, Groningen, the Netherlands: My wife of a few months, Valeria, and I have moved to a new country and into our new lab. Our alarm clock rings. It's about six o'clock in the morning. After a sleepy breakfast, we put on our waterproof jackets and trousers and get out our bicycles. We pedal hard against the wind and horizontal rain to get to the "Neuro*I*maging Center," where we still work today. Anita, the imaging technician, has no sense of humor for delays, but takes a sadistic pleasure in giving us the earliest possible scanning slot.

Minutes later, a young French woman named Joyce, dressed in a blue pajama-like outfit, lies down on a white bed in front of a large tunnel, headphones on her ears, head strapped down, and a large coil around her head like a birdcage. With a button press, Anita slowly moves her into the tunnel. Joyce is about to undergo testing in a functional magnetic resonance imaging (fMRI) scan, which will reveal different information from the earlier TMS studies, and, we hope, provide further evidence that humans have a mirror system for seen and heard actions.

The room with the fMRI machine pulses with the noise of the liquid nitrogen pumping to keep the magnet ~300°F below zero–the critical temperature range for superconductivity.

fMRI is a powerful method for measuring brain activity, based on the fact that if we use a particular part of the brain, this part needs more oxygen. To satisfy this demand, the body sends more blood to this particular brain region. By placing people into a strong magnetic field, it is possible to localize and measure this increase in blood flow, thereby indirectly measuring brain activity.

A heavy door closes behind us as Anita, Valeria, and I move to the control room. Valeria takes the microphone, "Remember, Joyce, listen carefully to the sounds you hear and if you hear a sound from the wrong category, press the button."

Anita puts Joyce's weight and anonymous study-participant number into the scanner's computer. A couple of mouse clicks later, a buzzing sound comes from the scanner room and a view of Joyce's brain appears on our screen. Valeria starts the stimulus computer, Anita the scanner. Instead of the buzzing noise from before, the scanner now produces a loud one-and-a-half second beep, then stays silent for four seconds, then beeps again, and so on. Between the beeps, Joyce hears various sounds through her headphones, such as a can of Coca-Cola being opened and poured into a glass, a zipper being undone, and a paper being ripped. After about twenty minutes, the scanner stops. Our computer screen shows slices of Joyce's brain, one by one.

A few minutes later, back in her regular clothes, Joyce answers a series of questions on a sheet of paper (see Appendix 1). "See you next week," Valeria tells her. Joyce nods. She has been in the scanner for us twice before. The first time, we showed her images of objects and hands. The second time, movies of actions, such as a human hand grasping a glass of wine, a hand closing a sugar box, but also a robotic hand doing the same actions. The next, and last, time she comes back we'll have her grasp objects, explore them with her mouth, and wiggle them between her toes.

WE UNDERSTAND ACTION SOUNDS THROUGH OUR OWN ACTIONS

A few weeks later, we hold our breaths while staring at the screen, awaiting the results of our first study in the Netherlands. One side of the screen shows the results of the trials in which participants, including Joyce, performed actions with their hands and with their mouths, and the other side shows the results when participants listened to such actions. What appears on the screen is almost too good to be true. The sound of the actions clearly activated the same brain areas as the execution of similar actions, albeit more weakly (Figure 3.1), which was exactly what we had hoped for if there were auditory mirror neurons in the human brain.

Now, to be useful, a mirror system would need to be selective. The sound of a particular action would need to activate an area involved in executing the same action. In the monkey, we had found that neurons with different preferences for particular actions were often very close to each other. A neuron selective for breaking was located less than two hundredths of an inch away from one for ripping. Unfortunately, it's not possible to see this level of detail with fMRI, because the limited spatial resolution divides the brain into three dimensional pixels, called voxels, which are about a tenth of an inch cubed and contain millions of neurons. Within such a voxel the signals from all the neurons blend together, so even if mirroring seemed to happen, determining selectivity of individual neurons is hopeless.

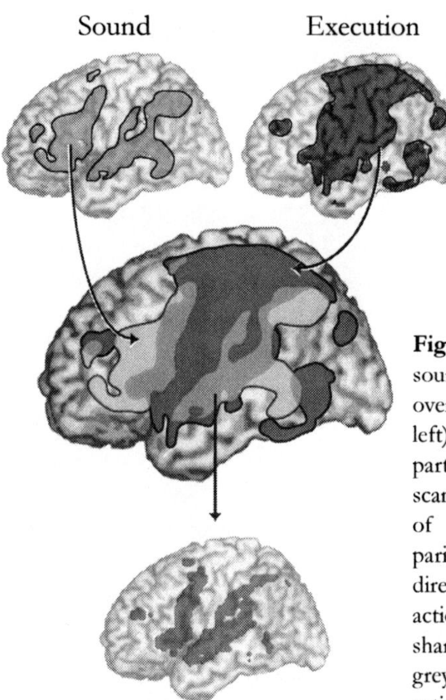

Figure 3.1: The activity caused by the sound of actions is shown as a light grey overlay on a profile vision of a brain (top left), next to the activity measured while participants execute actions in the scanner (top right). These two patterns of activations overlap in pre-motor, parietal and temporal areas (bottom). A direct com-parison (middle) shows how action-sounds and action-execution share 'mirror' brain areas (intermediate grey) while other areas are specific for actionsounds (light grey) and action-execution (black)

What we had found in monkeys is that, although the middle part of the premotor cortex where mirror neurons are found often responds to actions of the hand and the mouth, the top part of the premotor cortex contains mainly neurons responding to hand actions, and the bottom part, to mouth actions. In these top and bottom sectors, even with the limited spatial resolution of fMRI, one could thus expect that the top parts should respond more strongly when people perform actions with their hands, and when they hear the hand actions of others, but less strongly if they perform or hear actions performed with the mouth. The opposite should be true for the bottom sector.

Looking more carefully at our data, this is exactly what we find[9]. Vast sectors of the premotor cortex were activated when people performed both hand and mouth actions, but the top part was more active for the hand and the bottom for the mouth. The same pattern was true during listening.

We are really excited about that finding. Only two years after we had established the existence of an auditory mirror system in monkeys, we can see with fMRI that a similarly selective system appears to exist in humans.

The fMRI study alone cannot prove the existence of auditory mirror neurons in humans because this method has a limited spatial resolution. The fact that the same location on an fMRI image is active during the perception and the execution of an action *can* be due to the fact that mirror neurons are active in the two cases. In theory, it could however also be that two separate sets of neurons without mirror properties are involved, one set only responding during the perception of other people's actions, and a neighboring, but different set, only involved during the execution of the same actions. Given that a neuron measures less than a hundredth of a millimeter and fMRI has a resolution of about two millimeters, these two alternatives cannot be distinguished using this method alone. To draw an analogy: I used to believe, as a child, that each pixel of our television was capable of showing all possible colors of the visual spectrum. Once I took a magnifying glass to look at it more closely and discovered that each pixel is actually constituted by different elements, each of which can only represent a single basic color. Could something similar be true for our fMRI voxels?

Two reasons, led us to believe that the results of the fMRI experiment were indeed due to mirror neurons. First, the premotor cortex, which responded during both execution and the sound of actions, corresponded to the areas where we found auditory mirror neurons in monkeys, suggesting that it may also contain mirror neurons in humans. Second, the TMS study proved that somewhere in the human brain, motor neurons must respond to the sound of actions, because in order for the motor response in the participant's hand to add the sound and TMS pulse together, the auditory signal had to somehow converge onto the motor signal of the hand. The fMRI experiments showed that the most likely location for that convergence is in mirror neurons in the premotor cortex. In sum, the fMRI study showed us *where* they converged, the TMS study *that* they converged. If we had not shown the existence of auditory mirror neurons in the monkey, people might still have doubted the finding, but all together, this made the existence of these neurons in humans a quasi-certainty.

Since then, a vast number of studies confirmed this conclusion further. The most spectacular of these is a study published in 2010 by my colleagues Roy Mukamel and Marco Iacoboni at UCLA together with the neurosurgeon Itzhak Fried at UCLA. Itzhak Fried is a neurosergeon that helps people with medication resistant epilepsy. If he suspects that a particular brain region is the source of the epilepsy, he implants small electrodes in this region for a couple of days to acertain his suspition. If these electrodes indeed measure spontaneous epileptic activity, he can remove the region surgically to cure the epilepsy. During the period of recording that can last several days, patients simply lie in bed and wait for spontaneous seizures to happen. Meanwhile the electrode that is implanted for medical reasons can provide neuroscientists the unique opportunity to directly listen to the activity of single neurons in the human brain without causing any increased risk for the patient. Many patients suffering from neurological problems such as epilepsy are eager to promote a better understanding of the brain and volunteer to participate in scientific experiments. Roy Mukamel and Marco Iacoboni therefore decided to investigate if they could directly record the activity of mirror neurons in humans through these electrodes. The medical indication lead to many patients having electrodes in the supplementary motor area (SMA), a motor region that is not unlike the premotor cortex where mirror neurons were first recorded from in monkeys. To their excitement, Roy and Marco found that several neurons in this motor region where not only active while the patient grasped small objects but also while viewing movies of other people grasping similar objects. Several other neurons responded both while the patient was asked to make certain facial expressions and while viewing the facial expressions of others[10]. Altogether these experiments now provide uncontestable evidence that humans have mirror neurons too[11].

THE MIRROR SYSTEM INCLUDES SEVERAL BRAIN REGIONS

Studies using fMRI and positron emission tomography (PET) scans have shown precisely where in the brain activity is induced both during the sight/sound and the execution of actions. Two of the regions involved, the premotor cortex and the posterior parietal lobe, are the same two areas where mirror neurons have been found in monkeys.

A third area of common activation is in the visual cortex of the temporal lobe. Together with David Perrett, I examined the properties of neurons in that area while getting my doctorate in Scotland. Neurons in the monkey in the visual cortex respond to the sight of faces and facial expressions, to the sight of movements of the human body, and to the sound of actions. But unlike mirror neurons in the premotor and parietal lobe, neurons in this visual area do not respond while the monkey executes actions. Hietanen and Perrett examined the neurons that respond to the sight of a hand moving upwards and found that when the monkey lifted his own hand, only half of these neurons responded strongly to the sight[12]. If the neurons were only visual, they should have responded equally to both sights. In a way, it makes sense that they do not. If I move my hand, I do not need to be very aware of the sight of a hand moving, since I already know that I am doing it. To achieve this down-regulation of my own movements, the brain would need to send a copy of the motor signal that moves my hand to the temporal lobe and selectively inhibit those neurons with corresponding visual properties. The process requires energy and may be what augments the blood flow in the visual cortex while participants in the fMRI studies execute actions.

Tickling captures the experience of subtracting our own motion from the processing of sensory signals. Sarah-Jayne Blakemore, who has studied tickling extensively, built a tickling machine[13]. Participants tickled themselves by moving a joystick that controlled a little robot. If the robot moved in synchrony with the joystick, the person felt no tickling. If Sarah-Jayne introduced a delay between the movement of the joystick and the robot, participants could suddenly tickle themselves, indicating that the cancellation of our own movements is a very selective process that deletes the exact consequences of what we do from our sensory input. If the consequences are delayed in time, they can escape the selective gating, and we can tickle ourselves.

An interesting property of this cancellation is that it requires the inverse process of that used in mirror neurons. Mirror neurons translate a sensory stimulus (an action I see) into a motor vocabulary (the action I can do). However, to cancel the consequences of our own movements, the brain needs to transform a motor action I'm planning to do into the *sensory* vocabulary of what I will see, in order to subtract it from a visual description. The brain thus translates back and forth between motor and sensory vocabularies, which also has the advantage that if our movement does not look like what we expected, the process will nullify the aspects we expected, but leave the ones we have failed to predict uncanceled and salient, providing a valuable "error" message. I remember waking up one morning with Valeria, side-by-side, lying on our backs with our legs intertwined. I looked down at our feet, and was convinced that one of the feet was mine. But when I tried wiggling it, another foot moved! This sight felt very odd, very surprising. My motor program had somehow erased the movement of the wrong foot, leaving the sight of that other wiggling foot oddly salient.

The overall mirror circuitry is thus composed of a core circuit of premotor and parietal areas containing mirror neurons, and a third area in the temporal lobe, intimately linked to the other two areas. This area in the temporal lobe provides visual input to the core mirror areas and in return receives information about motor intentions that it uses to cancel expected visual consequences. The situation resembles very much the situation in the monkey (Figure 3.2), suggesting that the macaque and human mirror system may indeed stem from a common ancestor. Given that, as we have seen, the function of a neuron is determined by its connections, to understand the mirror system we need to understand what connections allow the neurons in this system to have mirror properties.

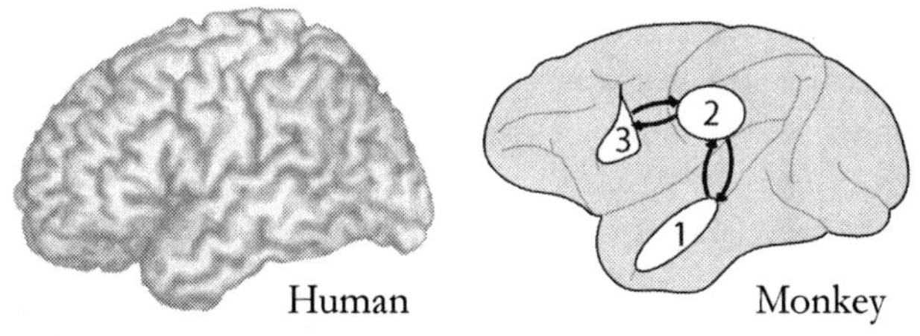

Figure 3.2: In both humans (left) and monkeys (right), the mirror neuron system involves a high-level visual area in the temporal lobe (1), a parietal area (2) and the premotor cortex (3). In the monkey we know that neural connections exist between 1 and 2 and between 2 and 3 but not between 1 and 3.

The matter of how mirror neurons receive input is not trivial. In monkeys, connections can be studied using very precise methods. One technique uses the plant horseradish, which contains an enzyme called horseradish peroxidase, or HRP, that has the peculiar property of being taken up by neurons, and being actively transported by the neuron in the direction opposite to the normal information flow. Neurons sum their inputs in their body and if it exceeds a certain threshold, send an action potential along their axons as output, which finishes on a synapse, where the activity is communicated to the next neuron. HRP, on the other hand, is transported by the neuron in the opposite direction, from the synaptic termination, back along the axon, to the cell body. If you inject HRP into a monkey's premotor cortex, it is transported backwards to the parietal lobe. Interestingly, if you inject it in the parietal lobe, much of it is transported back toward the premotor cortex, showing that the two areas are mutually connected, but some of it is also transported toward the visual cortex. Injections in this visual cortex in turn lead to transport back to the parietal lobe, revealing another mutual connection.

Together, these studies suggest that when we watch the actions of others, the visual signal travels from the eye through a series of visual processing steps that lead to the activation of visual neurons in the temporal lobe where neurons respond to the sight of bodily movements and facial expressions. From there the signal goes to the parietal lobe and from there to the premotor cortex. Along these passages, the visual information is translated into an increasingly motor information, as in both the parietal and premotor areas mirror neurons are found that are also active during motor execution. During motor execution, the opposite flow of information appears to occur. The motor activity in premotor and parietal areas is sent backwards to the visual cortex to cancel out expected consequences of our own actions.

Mirror neurons use this system to facilitate working with others to perform coordinated tasks. For example, if I ask you to help me move a dinner table when it has already been set, it will need to be kept level. I start lifting the table, which generates a flow of information from my premotor areas to my visual cortex. At the same time I see you starting to lift the table as well, which creates a flow of information from your premotor cortex to your body and from there to my eyes, my visual cortex and my premotor mirror neurons. The sight of your lifting activates my own lifting mirror neurons, which facilitates the execution of my correct reaction to lift the table further to keep it level, which will in turn cause information from my premotor cortex to flow to my visual cortex but also from my premotor to your visual cortex as you monitor my movements, and so on. The whole action is not so much a sequential information exchange, but two brains becoming a single interconnected regulation process. What links our brains is the way mirror neurons lead both to actions and perception of the other's actions. From the brain's perspective, the outside world, composed of our bodies and the table, becomes an interface between our brains, and the complex information flow is so finely tuned that we can often manage not to spill a single drop of wine from the glasses on the dinner table.

Millions of years of evolution have come up with this exquisite system that enables us to take the great evolutionary leap of doing together what we could have never done alone. At the beginning, these interactions may have involved moving heavy objects, hunting large animals, or coordinating our defenses. Now it involves building space shuttles in teams of thousands of people, and developing our technological cultures by working together and learning from one another.

EMPATHIC INDIVIDUALS MIRROR MORE

Inherent in the idea of a mirror system, is the concept that people who are more empathic should have a stronger mirror system. Not all of us are equally empathic. Some people watch movies like *Dr. No* without any discomfort while the spider crawls over Bond's chest. Others are so affected by it that they have to turn away and cover their eyes. How empathic are you? If you turn to the end of this book, in Appendix I, you can fill out a questionnaire developed by Mark Davis of the University of Texas at Austin[14, 15]. Based on your answers, the test will tell you how empathic you are.

If you obtained a very high empathy score you might guess that your brain mirrors the actions of other people very strongly. If you have a low score, you might expect the opposite. These are exactly the results we found[9]. We had Joyce and the other participants in our fMRI experiment fill out the same questionnaire. We then selected the six individuals that scored highest on the Perspective Taking scale and the six that scored lowest, and measured how much both sub-groups activated their own actions while listening to the actions of others. The results were striking. Whereas the six participants that scored high on Perspective Taking showed strong mirror activations in the areas involved in performing hand actions, the six participants that scored low on Perspective Taking did not show any significant mirror activity (see Figure 3.3)[9]. This was the first demonstration that differences in the mirror system for actions go hand in hand with how easily people slip into the skin of other people.

Interestingly, not all the aspects of empathy predicted equally well whether someone was going to have strong activations in the mirror system. Unlike the Perspective Taking scale, the more emotional aspects of empathy captured by the Emotional Concern and Personal Distress subscales did not predict whether people had strong or weak mirror activations. Thus, activations in the mirror system for actions seem to have more to do with understanding the goals and motivations of others, as measured by Perspective Taking, than with sharing their pain or distress.

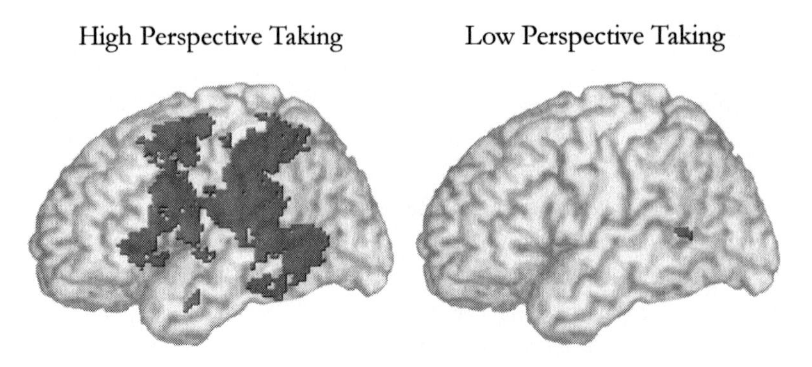

Figure 3.3: While people with high Perspective Taking scores acti-vate their mirror system intensely while theylisten to the sound of the actions of other people (left) people with low Perspective Taking score do so much less (right).

If you have a low Perspective Taking score, it does not mean you lack a mirror system. If you really try to feel what it would feel to do the same action you just heard, your mirror system would also become active. If you do not try to do so, however, more empathic individuals recruit their own actions more strongly.

What we still do not understand is *how* a score on a Perspective Taking scale is linked to activity in your mirror system. Mirror neurons are the result of a particular pattern of connections between visual, auditory, and motor-related regions of the brain. It might be that the stronger the connections, the more automatically we share the actions of others, and the more we are drawn into seeing things from their perspective. According to this view, people that have to look away from violent scenes in movies would do so because their connections are stronger.

On the other hand, it might be that the basic connections are not the critical issue. Instead, other brain mechanisms may modulate our sharing of actions, including selective attention. If you direct the spotlight of your mental attention onto a particular aspect or location of the world or your own body, the neural response to the objects in that focus is increased at the cost of the neural representations of other aspects. Experiments in monkeys actually show how strong the effect of selective attention can be. If the monkey's task is to ignore horizontal lines, and press a button only when vertical lines start to blink, responses in the visual brain areas to the unattended horizontal lines will almost entirely disappear, as if selective attention had erased the horizontal lines from the image[16]. Meanwhile, the response to the vertical lines is increased. Maybe participants with high Perspective Taking scores simply pay more attention to the actions of other people, thereby increasing the processing of these actions in the visual and auditory cortex. These stronger activations are then sent through the connections of the mirror system, leading to stronger mirror activations even without needing stronger connections.

These two possibilities will need further exploration, as they have very different implications in terms of how much we can manipulate the strength of the responses in our mirror system. Connections are difficult to modify, but attention can be redirected more flexibly and is easily accessible for cognitive behavioral procedures.

4

Born to Socialize

The discovery of mirror neurons was a true surprise for most scientists. They allow us to peek into the tricks the brain uses to understand other people. Just like most of us would agree that a basic knowledge of physics and engineering makes an airplane pilot safer and more efficient, knowing about the basic workings of mirror neurons allows us to be a little more cunning in our social world.

Learning how to perform an action changes our perception

In a classical view of the brain, the process of understanding other individuals relies on specialized systems in the brain that are separate from those responsible for our own actions. This suggests that your own motor skills should have limited and indirect influences on your perception of other people's behavior. In the light of mirror neurons, the situation is quite different. If we interpret the actions of other individuals through our own motor programs, our motor programs will have a very strong impact on our perception of other individuals. Valeria, my wife, has been playing the piano for over ten years. Does that make listening to a piece of piano music feel different for her compared to someone like me, who has never played? It sure does! She can transform the sound into the motor program for playing it, but I cannot.

Marc Bangert and his team at the University of Hanover in Germany studied this phenomenon in 2006. They compared a group of people that had never played the piano with a group that had played intensively for many years. Both groups listened to recordings of a piano concert while the scientists measured their brain activity. Although activity in premotor areas was almost absent in the participants that had never played the piano, experienced piano players automatically activated the premotor programs involved in piano playing. Somehow, by learning to *play* the piano, they had changed the way they *hear* piano music. Suddenly, they not only heard the piano through their ears but also started to perceive it through the movements of their own fingers, which was not the case for the musical novices[17], suggesting that the auditory mirror system we measured with the sounds of actions can be extended to novel actions, such as playing a musical instrument. Our mirror system is thus not fully determined at birth, but can be augmented by experiences that change the way we perceive these actions in others.

The increase in mirror response with expertise could be due to either the fact that piano players are very interested in piano music and hear a lot of it, or the fact that they play a lot of piano. To disentangle these possibilities, the same year, the Spanish neuroscientist Beatriz Calvo-Merino and her colleagues at the University College London turned to ballet dancers. Female and male dancers train together, so they see each other's movements very frequently, and although many moves are common to male and female dancers, some are not. The gender-specific movements are thus an opportunity to distinguish the effect of seeing actions, and being interested in them, from the effect of performing actions. When the researchers showed gender specific movements to expert male and female dancers, both sexes showed some degree of mirror activity to all movements, but the females showed stronger mirror activity to the female movements, and the males to the male movements[18].

The difference in reactions suggests that the mirror system can respond to movements, the details of which are not in your own vocabulary, just like the so-called broadly congruent mirror neurons encountered in previous chapters. However, a stronger mirror response occurs at the sight of a movement that has been practiced over and over again.

The discovery of the mirror system has thus provided a new perspective on the familiar experience of, after learning a novel sport, finding the sport much more involving to watch on television. We can still perceive the basic movements of sports and activities we have never performed, but activities we have been trained in are perceived in a richer way.

I still remember the effect that my fencing courses had on me. Before learning to fence, watching the sport during the Olympic Games fascinated me, but I couldn't really understand what was going on. Everything was a blur. After two years of fencing, I am still not much of a swordsman, but my perception has sharpened with my skills. I now see more clearly what the fencers do. Their movements have started to make sense to me–and sometimes I find it almost impossible not to move while watching a cunning lunge. Parts of my body now seem to help my eyes see what they could not see before.

Some simple advice can be culled from these observations. If you truly want to understand particular actions of other individuals, don't just study, but *acquire* their skills, and you will understand them much better. Referees in sports, musical critics, sports' therapists, and many other professionals should all benefit from realizing that there is a tight causal relationship between their motor skills and their perception.

THE MIRROR IN OUR BRAIN EVEN RESPONDS TO ROBOTS

While watching the Star Wars saga, most of us attribute a whole range of human emotions to R2D2 and C3P0, although we rationally know that robots are controlled by computers that have no emotions. With other humans, we intuitively feel that they have an inner life that resembles our own, so we attribute the feelings we have while performing such actions to the other human beings performing the same action. We decided to study what our brain does while viewing the actions of robots.

Back in the lab, we showed our participants, including Joyce, movies of not only a human performing everyday actions, but also of an industrial robot performing the same actions. The robot grasped a cup of coffee and a glass of wine, and scooped soup out of a bowl, but did so in the way an industrial robot would, with straight movements of constant velocity. Its claw looked more like R2D2's arm than a human hand. We were looking to see if the human mirror system would treat the movie of an industrial robot grasping a glass in the same way as it would the movie of a fellow human being.

The answer is yes[19]. Watching the robotic movies activated the mirror system as much as the human movies did. The differences in the movement pattern and physical appearance between the robot and our human observers did not prevent the mirror system from interpreting the robotic action in the light of the participant's own, human actions. This was true even if, instead of the highly human action of taking a glass, the robot simply moved colored wooden blocks. Another experiment showed that we also interpret the actions of animals through our own actions[20].

In a world in which robots become increasingly important, this capacity of the mirror system to assimilate robotic actions has an important implication. Our brain has evolved over millions of years to deal in optimal ways with the behavior of other human beings and animals. The observation that robots, even if they do not look like humans, appear to activate our mirror system much like fellow humans do means they could, in the future, be integrated into the work force and tie into the mirror system of human workers, thereby taking full advantage of millions of years of evolution. Further experiments along this line will be required to establish the limits of this phenomenon. Movie makers like George Lucas appear to have had a good hunch. Even very odd-looking robots can tie into our social brain, and make us feel pity, compassion and joy, almost as if they were human.

HOW PEOPLE BORN WITHOUT HANDS MIRROR HAND MOVEMENTS

One day, Theo Mulder, head of the Dutch Royal Academy of Science, and professor for movement science burst into our office with a big smile. "Would you be interested in scanning participants that were born without arms?" he asked. A flash of interest appeared in Valeria's eyes. She had just finished analyzing the data on robots, and kept wondering how would we perceive hand actions if we had never had hands? So of course we said yes.

A couple of months later, the first of our participants arrived. "Nice to meet you," he said and, while standing, lifted his foot to shake my hand. I shook his foot, amazed at how skillfully he moved his legs and feet. While Valeria explained the experiment to him, his left foot scratched his five o'clock shadow. "That sounds easy," he said, and minutes later he was in the scanner.

First, he watched movies of hands performing actions, then of hands and feet performing actions, such as a hand placing sugar in a coffee cup, and then a foot doing the same. At the end, in order to map his motor representation of mouth and foot actions, we had him move his lips and his feet. Shortly thereafter, the second participant arrived. I now shook his foot as if it were the most natural thing in the world. The experiment ran smoothly again, and off they went. Both participants are in their thirties, have demanding jobs, and were born without arms and hands.

A while later we were sitting in front of our computers again, looking at the results. They showed perfectly normal mirror activations in the same area where participants with hands and arms have their mirror activations. However, looking at the data while they had performed actions with their mouth and feet, it turned out that the sight of the hand action they had never performed was mapped onto regions of the brain they now use for their foot or mouth actions. Again, it appeared as though their mirror system recognized the purpose of the action, "grasping," and mapped it onto their own motor program for grasping that uses their foot or mouth. Interestingly, their foot representation had also invaded the territory that, in typically developed individuals, deals with hand execution, a phenomenon often observed in patients with amputation, explaining why the visual activity was in the same region as in normals. The regions of the brain that formerly dealt with the now missing limb start to represent adjacent body parts – and responds when they see other people do actions they would perform using that limb.

MIRROR SYSTEM FACILITATES UNDERSTANDING OF GOALS

Our motor system is composed of the primary motor cortex and higher motor areas, including the premotor cortex where mirror neurons are found. Neurons in the primary motor cortex are tied to particular muscle groups. If we look at all the cases in which a particular neuron in the primary motor cortex fires, we see that they are all cases where a particular muscle group worked in a particular way. For example, the muscles moving your index finger will be involved in typing on a keyboard, holding a cigarette, and making a "come here!" gesture. There is no purpose in common to all these movements, but the muscle movement is similar.

If we do the same for a premotor neuron, we see that common to all the instances of firing is a goal or purpose, such as grasping, breaking, or removing. Goal is used here in a pragmatic fashion, as that which the action aims to achieve. If I remove the cap from a fountain pen, the goal is for the cap to be no longer on the pen, whether I do so with my hands or mouth. Neurons in the premotor cortex appear to be organized in terms of such goals, with many responding similarly to grasping, independent of how it is performed. An fMRI study showed that writing with your hand or foot recruits the same regions of the premotor cortex[21].

Taken together, you could say that the motor system is organized like an army, which gives the brain great flexibility. Generals in the premotor regions decide what to do, junior officers at the transition from premotor to primary motor neurons decide how to achieve this goal within the constraints of a particular setting, and soldiers in the primary motor cortex then make the action happen by moving the right muscles. The flexibility is useful because, though eating always involves grasping then chewing then swallowing, how you grasp will change from time to time. Thus, it is wise to store the general program in the premotor cortex and then flexibly involve different muscles according to the situation, whether you have chopsticks, forks, or bread in front of you.

With the discovery of mirror neurons in the premotor cortex, the fact that this region contains generals and junior officers that think in terms of goals and not soldiers that think in terms of muscle groups becomes directly relevant for our perception of the actions of other individuals. As we have seen in the context of the experiments on robots, animals, and individuals born without arms, our mirror system appears to activate motor programs that would enable us to achieve the goal performed by the observed individual. If we see a robot grasp a glass, we activate motor programs that would make us grasp the glass with our hands. If participants born without hands see movies of someone grasping a glass, they activate motor programs that would use the foot or the mouth to achieve a similar goal. Within our knowledge of the goal-oriented representations in the premotor cortex, this result should come as no surprise. If one were to believe in a more classical model of the brain, in which the actions of other individuals are represented in a way that is independent from our own actions, it would be a lot more difficult to comprehend why goals seem to be the unit of interest in our observation of other individuals.

LEARNING BY OBSERVATION

The discovery of mirror neurons has also profoundly changed the way we think of another fundamental human capacity, learning by observation. As children we learn a lot by observing what our parents and friends do. Newborns, in the first week of life, have an inborn tendency to stick out their tongue if their parents stick out theirs[22]. Such imitation is not perfect. You may not see the tongue stick out each time you stick yours out at your newborn, but if you do it many times, the tongue will come out more often than if you do something different. Babies babble and later start to imitate the sounds their parents produce. Later still, they play with vacuum cleaners and hammers in imitation of their parents.

Our modern cultures, in which we write, speak, read, build spaceships and go to school, can work only because we are not restricted to the behavior we are born with or learn by trial and error. We can learn a lot by simply watching others. Cultural transmission refers to this amazing capacity to acquire skills and knowledge rapidly from other people. The culture of the Stone Age, for instance, required the capacity to learn how to make a blade out of a rock. Examination of blades of that era reveal that they were made according to relatively fixed procedures, which were perfected slowly over thousands of years—a clear indication of cultural transmission. Our current lifestyles depend enormously on such cultural transmission. Working on a new job often means learning how to perform a whole range of skills quickly by simply watching a more experienced person do them. Deprived of a capacity to learn by observation, our modern worlds would never have developed. Without it, any innovation serves only the innovator, and the knowledge dies with its discoverer.

Although we all take the capacity to learn from other people for granted, before the discovery of mirror neurons, scientists were struggling with the problem of how the brain could do that in the first place. What is even more striking is that the field had focused on what is called "true imitation.". It is only since World-War II, that science really tries to understand how animals learn. William Thorpe, reader at Cambridge University was one of the founding fathers of this new discipline. But according to his influential definition, true imitation is "copying a novel or otherwise improbable act."[23]. A secret agent peeking over the shoulder of someone typing in a password and then typing in the same password to gain access to a computer would not be truly imitating because he has typed numbers on keypads before, and the act is thus not novel. On the other hand, if I show a child how to make a funny grimace, by forming a pair of pilot's goggles with my hands and putting them on my head in an odd movement, copying it would be true imitation, because the act in itself is novel and improbable. According to this strict definition, finding evidence for imitation in animals is difficult, although probably not impossible.

With the discovery of mirror neurons, understanding how we learn to perform an action by observing someone else perform a similar action becomes a tangible problem. Mirror neurons activate the observer's own way of performing an action while observing someone else perform a similar action, and this is particularly important while reproducing the actions of other individuals[6]. What is even more important, though, is that knowing that the mirror system is goal oriented suggests that during observation we do not so much learn the arbitrary details of how the demonstrator achieved the goal, but rather what he has achieved or tried to achieve. Young children are already rational in their reproduction. If you have your hands full and press a button with your head, they will press the button with their hands, demonstrating the tendency the mirror system would predict. Whereas strictly congruent mirror neurons could provide a somewhat more detailed description of how the action was performed, the less specific, goal oriented, broadly congruent mirror neurons are about twice as frequent as strictly congruent mirror neurons[24], and goals are thus the dominant variable within the mirror system.

Following Thorpe's definition, many primatologists, in search of evolutionary precursors of cultural transmission, focused on examining the existence of true imitation in animals. Generally, monkeys fail to show robust evidence of such true imitation. For a while this was seen as in apparent contrast to the presence of mirror neurons in these animals, but this seems, in fact, to be a misinterpretation of the function of mirror neurons. Mirror neurons predict that monkeys should be able to learn by observation, but not necessarily reproduce the detailed way in which the goal was achieved.

Francys Subiaul and his colleagues of the Department of Anthropology at Columbia University examined the presence of learning by observation in a simpler sense in monkeys[25]. They placed two monkeys side-by-side, each in front of its own touch-screen computer. The computer showed the monkeys four images somewhere on the screen, and if they touched the pictures in the right order, they received some fruit juice. But first they had to figure out the right order. In the trial-and-error condition each monkey had to discover the correct sequence by himself. In the social learning condition, one of the monkeys could watch a more experienced monkey execute the correct sequence in front of him. It turned out that, although it took a monkey about twenty attempts to get a sequence right if alone, after viewing another monkey perform the task correctly, only fifteen attempts were needed. The monkey learned something from simply watching the behavior of the other monkey.

The mirror neurons' contribution in such tasks is to activate a certain sequence of well-known actions in the brain of the observing monkey. To learn the sequence, in addition to these mirror neurons, systems are required that remember the order of the actions, which is an additional capacity humans master much better than monkeys.

Humans would require many fewer than 15 attempts after watching a skilled demonstrator. Both species intuitively share the actions they observe, but humans may remember the experience better and more accurately than monkeys.

A NEURAL BASIS FOR INTUITIONS

Philosophers like Descartes have told us that the mind of another person is an invisible, obscure, and impenetrable entity. Popular wisdom has it that beyond logical knowledge there are other ways to feel what goes on in the minds of others. For a long time, terms such as "(female) intuition," which reflect the idea that one can "tune" into the minds of other people, appeared to be superstitious nonsense, far removed from respectable science. But the discovery of mirror neurons has changed the way we conceive of the relationship between individuals. While we witness the actions of others, our own premotor cortex resonates as if it was doing the actions we observe. The mirror system builds a bridge between the minds of two people and shows us that our brains are deeply social.

In our fMRI experiments, the participants were not explicitly asked to place themselves in the shoes of the people whose actions they were listening to or observing. After the experiments, we asked them if they deliberately imagined being the people they saw, and none of them told us they had. The mirror activity we observe, in which the premotor cortex resonates with that of the actors, is therefore a process that occurs without being associated with an effortful, volitional process of taking the perspective of other people. Instead, it appears to be a process that is spontaneously set in motion while we observe the actions of other individuals, which is what makes it seem so intuitive. We did not even try to enter the minds of others, and yet, we share their actions. In a way, we "feel" what goes on in their minds, which sets the mirror system apart from a detective's deliberate, thoughtful journey, into the mind of a fugitive.

The discovery of mirror neurons made it clear to me that our brains are indeed almost magically connected to each other. We are not born with a brain that deals exclusively with ourselves, but with one capable of feeling with other people. Our brain is set up to resonate with the people around us. In this light, my attitude toward my intuition has changed. I used to consider them unreliable and inferior to my rational thoughts but now I see them as the result of a very cunning and exquisitely evolved process that utilizes the richness of my own motor expertise to gain insights into other people. Isntuition has become like a faithful collaborator for me. I do not have to control and steer her work but I can trust her conclusions.

As demonstrated by the differences observed between people with different levels of empathy, and between people with more or less expertise in certain skills, the motor resonance that links our brains can vary in strength. One of the fascinating topics of future research will be to investigate how the strength of that connection can be manipulated. Scientists across the world now study how meditation and drugs can strengthen empathy, and how our decision to empathize or not to empathize with someone changes the activity in our mirror system.

Implications for teaching: an action is worth a thousand words

In our knowledge-based civilization, abstract knowledge is valued higher than any practical skill. Einstein, able to grasp the hidden laws of matter and the universe through a simple equation, $E=mc^2$, represents the ultimate genius that most people would be proud to be. Intellectual, abstract, rational thinking is often seen as the goal that schools should strive toward, with more practical and intuitive skills seen as less worthwhile.

In terms of teaching, the mirror system suggests that abstract theory might not always be the most effective way of teaching. Language, the most widely used teaching tool, has been evolving for at most two million years. Learning by observation on the other hand is a capacity that is many hundreds of millions of years old. What that means is that, by focusing on verbal teaching, a teacher neglects learning channels that are ancient and immensely effective. Mirror neurons open an exquisitely privileged door between the brain of a teacher and his students.

Verbal material in a textbook needs substantial effort to decode, and we recognize that what ends up in our heads, once we have understood the topic, is quite different from the long string of letters and numbers in the textbook. Learning from observation, on the other hand, feels direct and intuitive. Tying a knot while we have an experienced sailor slowly demonstrating the knot feels natural; trying to tie the knot based on a description in a book is a frustrating experience.

Learning by observation feels direct but, of course, it is not a simple process. The mechanical forces exerted by the fingers as we tie a knot are not any more similar physically to the waves of light reflected from the body of a demonstrator than to those reflected by the letters of a book. Indeed, despite decades of hard work, immensely powerful computers and some of the cleverest brains in the world, artificial intelligence is still struggling to build a robot that can imitate a wide variety of skills by observation. For robots, performing skills based on the written instructions of a computer program is much easier. What makes learning by observation more natural for us, and the computer program more natural for machines, is that we have evolved for hundreds of millions of years to be good at learning by observation whereas language is a new "add on" to our brain. Robots, on the other hand have evolved in a world of computer programs and learning by observation is the new "add on" for them. Mirror neurons and the relatively direct connections between the visual and auditory cortices that process the actions of other people are the embodiment of these millions of years of evolution. Not using this finely tuned system in teaching means neglecting an amazingly efficient channel of communication.

If we have to explain how to do something, demonstrating the skill may thus be an important didactic tool that complements a verbal explanation. For instance, learning in school how to solve simple equations seems not to be a bodily skill, yet our understanding is eased by transforming them into a more intuitive motor operation. For example, the concept of adding and subtracting can (and maybe should) always be supplemented by a bodily demonstration. Take a bowl of three candies, grasp two additional candies that lie next to the bowl, and place them into the bowl. "That is adding." Then grasp four from the bowl, and take them out of the bowl, and say, "That is subtracting."

Most of us have experienced how illuminating such demonstrations can be for understanding abstract concepts. Many good teachers naturally understand the importance of such demonstrations. The discovery of mirror neurons helps us transform the intuition of some gifted teachers into a more formal understanding of the importance of our bodies as channels of communication.

SIMULATION IS A FUNDAMENTAL PRINCIPLE OF BRAIN FUNCTION

As we have seen, a fundamental property of the mirror system is that viewing or hearing actions activates regions of the brain as if you were performing the same action. The brain simulates what it sees in the environment, but it is important to note that simulation is not just using the same brain areas for execution and perception. Some additional processes that translate seen/heard actions into a motor vocabulary are required, and mirror neurons are part of that transformation. In addition, the brain needs to avoid the situation where the results of the simulation sneak out of the brain and into the muscles of the body. Such output would be counterproductive. Punching fellow spectators while watching a boxing match would obviously be maladaptive.

It turns out that other brain regions, probably in the frontal lobe, come into play each time we watch the actions of others. The role of these areas is to close the 'gate' that normally transmits the orders of the generals in the premotor mirror neurons to the soldiers in the primary motor cortex. While we perform actions, this gate needs to be open, but while we simply watch the actions of others, it needs to be closed to prevent us from automatically acting out the actions we only want to be internally simulating. Some patients, called echopraxic (from the Greek words echo, meaning "repeat" and praxia, meaning "execution"), have damage to the frontal lobe and seem to lack the capacity to close that gate during observation. The French neurologist, François L'Hermitte, provided a powerful illustration of this disorder. He placed two pairs of glasses on a table, and asked his echopraxic patient to sit down. The patient was wearing his own glasses, but at the sight of the neurologist putting on one of the two spare pairs, the patient automatically picked up the other pair and placed it on top of those he already wore. Without the inhibitory activity of the frontal lobe, the patient was powerless in the face of the influence that other people's actions have on his motor system.

Once the brain can master the transformation of the sight and sound of actions into motor programs, and if it can also learn to prevent motor output during simulation, simulation becomes a remarkably elegant way of making sense of the behavior of others. Seen in this way as a computational mechanism, the mirror system has alerted us to a fundamental property of the brain: employing brain areas formerly devoted to a particular task (doing an action) in new, additional functions (perceiving that action).

Another prominent example of simulation is imagination. Imagine what it feels like to run along the beach on a summer's morning, with your bare feet splashing the cool shallow water at each step, and the breeze ruffling your hair. The vast majority of individuals are quite good at conjuring vivid images and sensations through the power of their imagination. Interestingly, imagining actions also increases brain activity in the premotor regions involved in executing similar actions–as if you truly were running on the beach. Thus, during both observation and imagination, our brain uses the premotor cortex to mentally re-enact an action without actually moving the body. We can imagine doing something very accurately and understand what other individuals do because we use the very same machinery then as when we perform the action.

Imagining actions, viewing actions, and hearing the sound of actions can thus all be seen as examples of simulation. The difference is what triggers the simulation. During imagination, the simulation is internally triggered through our will to imagine an action, whereas during action-observation or when listening, it is triggered by a stimulus in the outside world, such as the sight or sound of a similar action[26].

Before the discovery of mirror neurons, most people would have thought that imagining a situation and actually seeing the situation are quite different processes. The similarity of these processes in neural terms is a wonderful example of how brain science can remove conceptual barriers.

5

Language

Evolution behaves like a tinkerer who, during eons upon eons, would slowly modify his work [...] cutting here, lengthening there, seizing the opportunities to adapt it progressively to its new use [...] It does not produce novelties from scratch. It works on what already exists, either transforming a system to give it new functions or combining serial systems to produce a more elaborate one. [27], p1164

The blue banana with a hundred legs

Imagine a blue banana with a hundred legs. What this sentence has just done is use one of humanities most outstanding and at the same time mysterious capacities. Through language, we can, without much effort, seed ideas in other people's minds. You would probably have never thought of a hundred-legged blue banana in your life. And yet a simple phrase of forty-one letters that bears no resemblance whatsoever to a hundred-legged blue banana was enough to manipulate you into thinking the improbable.

We can think about an idea and, through ink and paper, plant it in hundreds of thousands of minds. Now, thinking of a hundred-legged blue banana is, admittedly, of rather little use or risk. But as we all know, the capacity of coming up with and spreading ideas has the power to change our lives, and even our societies, fundamentally. Simple words can save or kill millions, for example if they describe how to produce penicillin, gun-powder or—ironically—a perfect society.

What's more, language frees us from the here and now. Take

vervet monkeys, for example. Vervet monkeys have a very small, meaningful vocabulary of about a dozen grunts and calls. One of the calls signifies that there is a predator on land, such as a snake. As soon as a member of the group makes this snake-call, all the monkeys rush up the nearest tree. Another call signals a predator in the air, like an eagle, and as soon as the eagle-call sounds, all the monkeys sprint down the trees to seek refuge under bushes. Getting it right is critical, or you might end up in the belly of a snake. Compared to human language, the grunts of vervet monkeys have a fundamental limitation. Despite many years of field research, no primatologist has ever observed a mother vervet monkey grunting to her child the vervet equivalent of: "Listen, watch out for that hill over there, because that's where I've seen many snakes." All the calls made by vervet monkeys are made in the here and now, and they never combine them into sentences. Deprived of language, monkeys and apes need to learn either by their own experience or by directly watching someone else. A monkey can never share its past experience by telling another animal. We can. Through mouth-to-mouth communication at first, then books, and now the globe-spanning internet, knowledge is a verbal web that literally transcends space and time. I can consult Shakespeare's, Darwin's, and Newton's opinions just as easily as I can consult my late mother's recipes or the discoveries of a faraway colleague.

Perhaps astonishingly, no other animals have ever come up with a true language, but for almost all of us, acquiring the sublime skill of language is not that difficult, and certainly not like calculus or your annual tax declaration. By two years of life, we can utter orders, statements and questions. By four, most of us can speak in complex and grammatically correct sentences. And, despite inequalities in education, eighty percent of the world population can read and write by age fifteen[28]. Something hardwired in our brains seems to turn us into language-magnets, eager and able to learn this marvelous skill. We seem to have an innate instinct for language[29], and as we will see, mirror neurons may be a stepping stone to this instinct.

Intriguing evidence for just how strong this instinct is comes from deaf-born children in Nicaragua. Before the 1970s, children born deaf in Nicaragua usually stayed at home and had little contact with each other. In the late 1970s however, the government created schools aimed at teaching those children to lip-read Spanish. This failed, because learning to lip-read is, contrary to a wide spread myth, very difficult for people born deaf.

Instead, the real success happened outside of the classroom. Hanging around with other, normally hearing kids, the deaf children developed some "homemade" hand gestures to communicate. These gestures resembled those most of us use to describe simple things in a foreign country, like cupping your fingers around an imaginary glass and bringing it to your mouth to indicate drinking.

Then, when the deaf children came into contact with each other, they started to combine their limited vocabulary of gestures and gradually transformed these gestures into a true language–Nicaraguan Sign Language. Although these children had been isolated from any example of grammar, they spontaneously created a grammar of gestures themselves.

For instance, they created the segmentation of concepts of their own accord. If you describe the motion of a ball "rolling down" a hill, you verbally segment this motion in two units of meaning: rolling (action) and down (direction). In addition and contrast, you might accompany your speech with an iconic, non-segmented downwards rolling motion that resembles the visual appearance of the event itself.

In 2004, the psycholinguist Ann Senghas from New York's Columbia University reported examined how the deaf children of Nicaragua sign such an event. She found that the youngest members of the community in particular did not gesture in a single downwards-rolling motion. Instead, they used two gestures: one for rolling followed by one for downwards motion. By doing so, they spontaneously transformed the iconic gesture they could have observed from hearing people into a gesture with grammatical structure, signaling a ball rolling down a hill. Given their failure to learn to lip-read or read Spanish, the deaf Nicaraguans could not have learned the grammatical concept of segmentation from hearing people. They truly created a grammar *de novo*. The resemblance between their grammar and that of virtually all other known languages extends far beyond this example of segmentation, and suggests that our brains are designed in a way that makes particular forms of language and grammar easy to learn[29-31].

SEARCHING FOR LANGUAGE'S MISSING LINK

Language is, for a large part, what makes humans unique. What's nice for us is, however, a thorn in the eye of many evolutionary biologists. To understand the evolution of a trait, biologists normally look for living sister species or fossil remnants of extinct species that show how the trait slowly and continuously grew, starting from a species that entirely misses the trait, and moving to one that has partially developed it, and finally to one that has fully developed it. For example, to understand how we came to have two legs and two arms, biologists looked at existing animals and have found examples of fish that can walk, such as the little tropical fishes called mudskippers, which survive draughts by walking on their fins from one tide-pool to another. They have also found fossil remnants of fish like the tetrapodomorphic *Tiktaalik* that combine many of the features of fish with those of early four legged land animals[32].

Together this provides a convincing and plausible scenario. Fish were exposed to draughts, and those that could walk further on their fins survived while those that couldn't, died. Selecting those walking best for millions of years resulted in Tiktaalik and then in amphibians. As descendents of these walkers, we now have four extremities. Evolution thus did not suddenly transform a legless organism into a cheetah but tinkered, as Francois Jacob put it so nicely[27], with the fins fish had, to make ever better walkers. Mudskippers and *Tijtaalik* are the evidence for this scenario. Through chimpanzees that can, albeit clumsily, walk erect on their hind limbs, we can even understand how four-legged animals slowly evolved to bipedal humans. So far, so good.

When it comes to language though, we're in the dark. There seem to be no intermediate stages of language. There are neither living nor fossil records of species that speak a little and have a little bit of grammar. Vervet monkeys, as we have seen, never string their calls into sentences and therefore completely miss one of the most defining features of human language. What is more, on the family tree of primates, vervet monkeys are quite distant from us. Macaques and apes closer to us however don't even seem to make the kind of calls vervet monkeys make. They lack any sign of such an acquired verbal vocabulary. In the many years I have tried to train monkeys the same single task, for instance looking at the middle of a screen for fruit juice, I would have thought that they would have somehow told each other, back in the home cage, "Hey look, just stare at the cross in the middle of the screen!" And yet they never did . . .

The search for fossil evidence of a missing link for language is equally frustrating because, unlike the bones of our legs, words and gestures do not fossilize. When paleontologists found the bones of the hominid "Lucy" in the Awash valley of Ethiopia, they could date the old lady to about three million years of age. From the skeleton, they could deduce that she habitually walked on two legs, making her a missing link between quadrupedal apes and bipedal humans. But did Lucy speak? Did she use her hands like the children of Nicaragua to tell her daughter that she would be back soon? We have no idea.

But maybe it's not as mysterious as we think. Although hard facts are lacking, we do have some clues about the missing links to language–and mirror neurons are one of them.

A SCENARIO FOR THE EVOLUTION OF LANGUAGE

What we know for sure is that about five million years ago our ancestors looked a bit like chimps, walked on four legs and were men of few words–none to be precise. But tough times were starting. The climate was changing rapidly, getting colder and drier. In Africa, the lush rainforests our ancestors were accustomed to got smaller and an unfamiliar savanna took over much of the land.

Those of our ancestors that stuck to the old habits were forced together in ever-smaller patches of forest, where competition for food became fierce. They became chimps. Others accepted the challenge of change, and went out into the savanna, adopting bipedal locomotion and living close to the edge of the forest. Here, in this new environment, innovation was the key to survival. Food in the form of rabbits and nuts was plentiful, but rabbits ran fast and nuts were hard to crush with teeth alone. Something must have happened then to set us off onto an evolutionary course that culminated in modern language. I hypothesize that a sequence of four relatively small steps turned us from mute chimp-like animals to the talkative folks we now are.

Step 1: Teaching. Our ancestors already had, like today's monkeys and apes, mirror neurons. So when one of them discovered how to crush nuts with a stone, others accidentally observed him and then tried to copy the skills. At the brink of starvation, relying on such accidental observation, however, is dangerously slow.

At this point, a mutation arose, and the mother that carried that mutation stopped waiting for her offspring to see her crack a nut by chance. She realized that if she first got the attention of her children by looking them in the eyes, and then demonstrated the action in a somewhat exaggerated manner whenever the children's eyes were looking in her direction, they were able to crack nuts long before the other kids. Her kids, in turn, taught each other all the little techniques they discovered. As they accumulated knowledge, they were able to use the resources of the new environment faster and more effectively than others. The change from accidental observation learning to deliberate teaching is what the Hungarian developmental psychologists Gergely Csibra and Gyorgy Gergely call "natural pedagogy," and seems to be absent in existing non-human animals[33].

If a teacher had just one stone and nut to demonstrate the movement, she would give them to the pupil to work with, while making the movement without the stone and nut and producing the cracking sound that signals success with her voice. With this tendency to teach, opportunities to learn become ever more frequent, and brain size became the limiting factor. Those with the biggest brains started to prevail because they were able to discover and accumulate more skills. This era culminated with our ancestors mastering making knives by chipping flakes off just the right type of stones about two million years ago–our ancestor named *Homo habilis* ("the handy man") had stepped onto the scene.

Step 2: Verbal motor control. Sounds and gestures were important for teaching. But to improve the rate of survival, *Homo habilis* had to find ways to coordinate better, making group hunting more efficient. Simple vocalizations became orders, and those with greater control of their vocal tract became more successful senders of orders, and those more able to comprehend became more successful listeners.

Here, mirror neurons came into play. The neurons involved in producing an order were activated when one heard the order, thereby enabling our ancestors to understand what the speaker meant. Words imitating the sound of an action or animal probably played a central role in the beginning. They are called "onomatopoeia," and such words still persists in our modern language, including verbs like to *crack*, *munch*, *meow* and *roar*, as well as names for animals, like *crow*, *cuckoo*, *cicada*.

As the millennia passed, our brains continued to increase in volume, our throats became more like modern throats. You can see a similar change in human babies. As newborns, babies can swallow and breathe at the same time, but cannot produce many sounds. Later, they become better at making complex vocalizations, but the price they pay is that they can now choke.

Step 3: Symbols. Some of our ancestors came up with the idea that the sounds used didn't have to resemble what they were used for. Referring to a lion by roaring worked, but how do you refer to something that doesn't sound like anything, for example, a stick? So let's image an ancestor pointing at a stick, and when everyone looked at the stick, he said something more or less random like "spear." At first, nobody understood what he meant, but after hearing it over and over again, the group came to associate the word with the stick. Using this trick, there were no longer limits on what words could refer to.

Step 4: Hierarchical structures. After a while, our ancestors ran out of single sounds they could produce to refer to different objects. Everybody had combined motor programs like grasping, pealing, squashing and eating many times into complex rituals for preparing food and so on. Suddenly, our ancestors applied this strategy to sounds, and made new words by combining a number of sounds, consonants and vowels, combined first into syllables and then into words.

Then, our ancestors realized that when they did something, there was someone doing that action and something to which the action was being done. They started to use the combination skills of their actions on their words and, instead of uttering single words, began to combine them. They stuck to a certain order, matching the order of their actions, a characteristic that can still be seen in the word order of modern language. Although the subject, verb and object that make up a sentence could in theory have six different orders, the vast majority of language place the subject first and then follow with object and verb–just as our actions start as intentions within us (the subject) before we move our body to act on an object. These verbal skills made our ancestors amazingly effective, both at coordinating and at teaching each other. Around two hundred thousand years before the birth of Jesus Christ, modern man, *Homo sapiens sapiens*, was born.

At the core of this hypothetical scenario is essentially a single idea. Language is tied to the motor system and the mirror neurons within it. We use language to teach skills, and skills are in the motor system; we use our mouth to speak, and our mouth is controlled by the motor system. And finally, if the sequences of movements of motor rituals are the basis for the structure of language, again, the motor system and grammar are related.

If this idea were true, we should be able to find some evidence for a link between the motor system and language and we should be able to come up with a reasonable scenario of how the brain's motor system could prepare apes to become talk show hosts. It turns out that we have such evidence, first in genes, and second in mirror neurons.

LINKING THE MOTOR SYSTEM WITH LANGUAGE

One of the links between language and the motor system is a gene called FOXP2, which was discovered in 2001 by an inspiring young geneticist and friend of mine, Simon Fisher, and his team at the Wellcome Trust Centre for Human Genetics in Oxford. They were studying a British family, dubbed "KE," of which half the members have a peculiar congenital speech disorder[34]. Those affected have three deficits. First, they have difficulties producing complex sequences of movements of the face and the mouth. If you ask them to puff their cheeks, then bite their lower lip, then close their right eye, they, unlike most of us, will be slow, and make many errors. Their articulation is also dramatically affected, making their speech labored, slow, and sometimes even unintelligible. Repeating a word like "Thimble," which most four-year-olds can do effortlessly, will take them several attempts, and they may never get it just right. Second, they also have problems with grammar. If you tell them "the dog was bitten by the man," and ask them to select whether a picture of a dog biting a man or that of a man biting a dog describes the sentence, they are confused. Finally, they have problems associating symbols with meanings. For example, if you repeatedly show them a blue square labeled with the number 1 and a red square labeled with the number 2, they will still find it hard to understand that blue + blue = red[35].

Examining the DNA of the "KE" family revealed that they were perfectly normal–except for a single, rare mutation in the FOXP2 gene. For the first time, scientists had found a gene that was directly and selectively linked to language.

Now, they needed to find out how FOXP2 affects language. Scanning the affected family members with magnetic resonance imaging (MRI) identified that their problem lies mainly in the motor system, including the premotor cortex in which humans appear to have mirror neurons. Researchers also found that the gene regulates the plasticity of the synaptic connections important in improving motor control of the face and the mouth through learning.

FOXP2 is not unique to humans. Mice and songbirds have a similar, albeit slightly different gene. The mouse version of Foxp2 (geneticist use small letters for mice genes and capitals for the human genes–a bit of human ego) differs in three places from the human FOXP2, suggesting that three mutations have happened in the seventy millions of years of evolution that separates mice from man. In the rodents, we know that Foxp2 is essential for normal motor learning, since mice in which Foxp2 is deactivated are slower at learning new tasks. Since mice don't speak, something must have happened during these three mutations that made the gene important for language.

Surprisingly, these mutations did not happen at a smooth rate of one every twenty-three million years. Instead only one happened in the sixty-four million years that separates mice from the last common ancestor of man and chimp, which is a very slow rate of genetic change. Then, suddenly, two mutations happened in the six million years that remained, suggesting a twentyfold acceleration of evolution. The last mutation probably occurred in the last two hundred thousand years–just when modern humans were born.

The discovery and study of FOXP2 tells us two things. First, based on the conspicuously discontinous mutation rate of this gene, the final evolution of language, involving fluent articulation and grammar, may be quite recent in human evolution. Second, the fact that a single mutation in human FOXP2 affects mainly the regions of the brain involved in motor control, supports the idea that the motor system plays a key role in many aspects of language.

BRIDGING THE INEXPLICABLE GAP TO LANGUAGE

If I told you that a passionate tinkerer in 1100 AD used sticks, ropes and pieces of iron to build a car with a combustion engine, would you believe me? Of course not. Now if instead I told you that my father's friend, a passionate tinkerer, took two motorcycles, and transformed them into a car with a combustion engine, would you believe me? Possibly. What makes the second story more plausible is what the tinkerer had to start with. Two motorcycles are not yet a car, but we can believe that a single tinkerer can do the job. After all, he has all the supplies he needs.

Something similar is the case with language and the discovery of mirror neurons. In the early 1990s, before mirror neurons were discovered, we knew nothing about FOXP2 and very little about what the brains of monkeys and apes had to offer evolution in the creation of language. Then mirror neurons, which are active both while we perform an action and while we see/hear other people's actions, were discovered in the premotor cortex. What's striking is that this very brain region also becomes active if I ask you to speak or listen to speech. Indeed, the premotor cortex, its ventral part in particular, first became famous for its role in language a long time before we knew anything about mirror neurons at all–in the nineteenth century.

Back then, the French physician Paul Broca came across a patient named Leborgne, who was called "Tan-Tan" by everyone in the hospital because, although his understanding of language was good, he could only say one word, "tan." After Leborgne died, Broca autopsied his brain, and found that the lower parts of his left frontal lobe (encompassing the premotor cortex that contains mirror neurons) had been massively damaged by either syphilis or a stroke.

Broca proposed that this area, now called "Broca's area," gives us the ability to talk. Modern studies using fMRI and PET now suggest that the left ventral premotor cortex that contains mirror neurons serves two important language functions. The more anterior part seems to be particularly involved when participants have to produce or understand grammatical sentences, whereas the more posterior part seems essential for articulation and perceiving what syllables other people speak[36].

Mirror neurons in monkeys, therefore, are in a part of the brain that will later become essential for language, and they are in a location of the brain that FOXP2 modulates. They are in the right spot to play a role in the evolution of language—just as fish have their pectoral fins in the right location for them to be the precursors of the forelimbs of tetrapods.

Although in theory, this could just be a coincidence, other features of mirror neurons make them suitable protagonists in the evolution of language. They play a central role in all steps of the evolutionary scenario I proposed above.

FOUNDATION #1: REALIZING THAT A MESSAGE CAME THROUGH

Most of us do not spend a lot of time speaking to chairs or doors. And with good reason—they never react. Spouses at least *sometimes* react, so we speak to or yell at them. Our pets never speak back to us, but we still speak to them, because they at least react when we say something. Communication is linked to a feeling that the other side gets the message. And so is deliberate teaching. After a few attempts, we stop trying to teach our cat how to speak, but keep going with our children because we see that only the latter improve. Mirror neurons could play a particular role in establishing this sense of "getting a message through" even in our non-human ancestors.

The neuroscientists Sarah Marschall-Pescini and Andy Whiten of St Andrews University demonstrated this most elegantly in a film showing an interaction between two chimpanzees on an island of Lake Victoria in Uganda. You can watch the movie yourself at http://www.apa.org/journals/supplemental/com_122_2_186/SMarshall_Pescini_supplm_material.avi[37]. In the movie, Mawa, a five year old male and experienced nut-cracker, uses a stone in his left hand to hit a palm nut placed on another rock that serves as an anvil. He rhythmically moves the stone up and down to hit the nut. Baluku, a three year old male and relative novice at this skill, watches Mawa – and then starts to spontaneously mirror the behavior, moving his hand up in down in rhythm with Mawa.

Baluku's spontaneous mirroring is likely to be the result of his mirror neurons triggering these motor programs. The now visible imitation would in turn trigger mirror neurons in Mawa, that would re-activate the very same motor program he is currently executing to crack the nut. Mirror neurons thereby close a social loop from a motor program in the demonstrator to its imitation by the student, back to the original motor program of the demonstrator.

Animals, of course, frequently witness other animals reacting to them; when the vervet monkeys hide in the bush from eagles, the eagle can observe that behavioral reaction. What makes the nut-cracking loop special is the direct correspondence between the two individuals' actions. The "teacher" sees the "pupil" respond to his actions with the exact same actions. The pupil becomes a living mirror for the teacher.

However, it seems that monkeys do not fully realize this because they never explicitly teach their children how to perform a skill. Some change must have occurred in the primate brain that allows us to use the activity of mirror neurons to realize that our child's skills are a direct reflection of what we have just shown her. Thus, although mirror neurons cannot be the whole story, they are a solid foundation that makes the emergence of natural pedagogy as a first step of human language evolution a plausible act of tinkering instead of an inexplicable giant leap.

FOUNDATION # 2: HEARING IS DOING

Step 2 of our evolutionary scenario suggested that mirror neurons are key to the emergence of language because the neurons involved in producing an order become reactivated when listening to that order, giving us a feel for what was being said. In analogy to "learning by doing," language would rely on "hearing by doing."

In the 1950s, Alvin Liberman and his colleagues at the Haskins laboratory in Yale made a frustrating observation that made them hypothesize that hearing by doing might indeed be a fundament of language–the discovery of mirror neurons forty years later makes their idea stuningly modern.

Liberman and his colleagues decided to help war veterans that had lost eyesight by creating a reading machine. Back then, making a machine that could read text aloud with a human-like voice was science fiction. As an alternative, they built a machine that would substitute the letters of printed text with distinctive beeps and buzzes. To their frustration, in contrast to the 15-20 letters most of us can read or hear each second, people could never learn to recognize more than 2 or 3 beeps a second. Such a rate was acceptable to Morse code telegraphist in the nineteenth century, but reading a book like the one you are reading just now would take about 3 weeks of full time work at that rate–too slow to be useful. Why is it, Alvin and his colleagues wondered, that we can distinguish 15-20 letters but only 2-3 beeps a second? To answer this question, they took a closer look at the sounds that compose natural speech and how they are perceived.

Using spectrography, which shows the frequency of a sound across time, they created spectrograms, images that capture the main physical characteristics of a sound. Spectrography-playback allowed them to tinker with a spectrogram or even generate entirely artificial spectrograms, and play them back to people. Liberman and his colleagues discovered, to their dismay, that there is no fixed relationship between the physical characteristics of a speech sound and its perception. For instance, the consonants /k/ and /p/ are both "stop consonants," in which airflow is stopped during production of the sound, but for /p/ you close your lips, and for /k/ you push the back of your tongue against your palate. On a spectrogram, both /p/ and /k/ are visible as bursts of energy centered around 1440Hz. Given that consonants are always linked with vowels, Liberman examined how people perceive such a burst of energy in the context of different vowels. He found that the physically identical burst of energy was perceived as /k/ before /a/, but /p/ before /i/ or /u/.

The question of how the same sound can be perceived as different letters naturally arose. The reason may be, simply, that while speaking the only way to produce a 1440Hz burst before the vowel /a/ is to press your tongue against your palate, like you do for a /k/.

The only way to produce it before /i/ or /u/ is to close your lips, as you would for a /p/. Because of this and similar observations, he came to two conclusions.

His first conclusion was that we do not speak in individual letters, but the characteristics of subsequent vowels and consonants influence each other, meaning that we co-articulate. As a result, in the word "papa," there is evidence of the /a/ during the /p/ and of the /p/ during the /a/. Although this means we don't have to hear 15-20 individual letters each second, it also means computers struggle with speech recognition since they prefer simple signatures, such as 1440Hz=/p/.

Liberman's second conclusion, however, is much more relevant to the mirror system. He proposed that we do not recognize people's phonemes by simply listening to them, but by performing the vocal gestures we would use to produce these sounds. So if we hear 1440Hz before an /a/, we mentally flick the back of our tongue to the palate, because that is how we would produce that sound, and so we feel a /k/. His theory became famous as the motor theory of speech perception. We resolve the ambiguity of sound-to-letter conversions by motorically reenacting what we hear.

The motor theory of speech perception of course sounds very much like what mirror neurons do when they activate motor programs based on the sound of actions—the here action being of the vocal tract. Accordingly, the discovery of mirror neurons in general, and of auditory mirror neurons in particular, has resulted in a revival of Liberman's ideas and three lines of investigation now tightly link the perception of phonemes to the activity of the mirror system.

First, fMRI experiments show that listening to nonsense syllables activates the same regions of the premotor cortex used when you pronounce those syllables or move your lips, and corresponds to that in which we found auditory mirror neurons in monkeys[9, 38-40].

A second experiment using TMS also suggests a link between mirror neurons and language listening. I participated in such a study in 2003, while in Parma. One of my colleagues, Giovani Buccino, placed me in what looked like a dentist's chair with a spoon in my mouth and a bathing cap on my head. Feeling a little silly, I asked him what the spoon was for. "I've attached two little electrodes to it, so that I can measure the activity of your tongue muscles," he told me with a jovial smile. He then placed a butterfly-shaped TMS coil on my head, much like the one Lisa Aziz-Zadeh had used in the experiment on the sound of actions in chapter 3. "Just relax, and listen carefully to the words." After he left the room, I heard a voice saying words such as "baffo" and "birra." Each word was followed by the characteristic "tock" of the magnetic coil. Sometimes, I felt my tongue twitch. One hundred words later, Giovanni opened the door, took the spoon out of my mouth and explained what he was doing.

Inspired by the mirror neurons we were recording from in the monkey, he, together with Luciano Fadiga, the brilliant Italian neurophysiologist who, in Parma, had pioneered the use of TMS to study the mirror system, decided to examine whether *hearing* a word like "birra," which requires a lot of tongue movement, would make the tongue of the listener move, as Liberman's theory predicted. This is exactly what happened. Simply listening to a word with a double "rr," with the help of the TMS, facilitated the tongue movements of the subjects, including me, but listening to a double 'ff', that does not involve the tongue, did not[41]. People therefore really do transform the speech they hear into the motor program they would use to pronounce them.

Together with the fMRI evidence, this shows that we do activate motor programs through our auditory mirror system while listening to the speech of others, but the question is whether we need this activation to understand what they say. The answer seems to be yes–at least sometimes. For many years now, neurologists have observed that patients with damage to the left premotor cortex that controls their mouth movements have problems in perceiving phonemes, particularly if the distinction is difficult, for instance, because the environment is noisy. More recently, magnetic stimulation has been used to temporarily disrupt activity in the same region in healthy individuals. The effect of this manipulation lasts only for a couple of minutes, but during that time participants are impaired in their discernment of phonemes[42]. If asked to distinguish simple sounds however, they were unimpaired.

That said, the motor system is not always necessary for recognizing what other people say. If we hear the word 'dad' under optimal hearing conditions, we can rely on representations of the word in our auditory memory, just as we recognize the melody of our mobile phone without needing to parse it into individual sounds. Although this is a difficult task considering the variability between different speakers, even chinchillas, furry little rodents living in the Andes, can be trained to hear the difference between /d/ and /t/ in much the same way as humans—even though they are unable to pronounce either and therefore cannot rely on motor simulation. [43]. Whenever the distinctions are fine-grained and difficult, such as determining whether someone said "he ate snails" or "he hates nails" at a cocktail party, mapping the sounds on ones motor programs becomes essential. At the laborious beginning of language evolution, these mirror matching mechanisms may have been particularly important for speech recognition.

Mirror neurons may thus contribute to language evolution by providing a feeling of communication (Foundation #1), and by activating motor programs to the sound of other people's (vocal) actions so that we can feel what they say (Foundation #2). The fact that mirror neurons already exist in monkeys means that the emerging humans already had a basis for linking the spoken orders of others to their own motor program for uttering these orders. Again, mirror neurons by themselves are not enough for language, as indicated by the fact that monkeys do not speak. Additional changes in the brain, of which FOXP2 mutations are a part, are clearly necessary. However, in analogy to what Louis Pasteur said about scientific discovery, also in the evolution of language, chance favors the prepared mind. I would argue that by linking the sound of motor programs to their execution, the brain of the emergent humans was prepared for certain random mutations to endow them with language. Without the preparation of mirror neurons, these mutations would not have done the trick.

A key challenge for the coming years will be to understand what kinds of mutations are necessary to transform the monkey's auditory mirror system into a specialized system for language. An intriguing possibility might be the emergence of babbling. Around five months of age, human babies start to produce seemingly random sounds with their mouth. They play with their own vocal apparatus, much like a child plays with a piano by pressing the keys at random to find out what they do. Each time the infant presses one of the imaginary buttons of his motor system and produces a sound, the sound and the motor program become associated with each other because they happen together–much as Pavlov's dog associated the sound of a bell with food because they always happened together. When the infant later hears his father say: "daddy," over and over again, this word will contain some of the phonemes the infant had randomly generated during babbling. Much like the sound of the bell later made Pavlov's dog salivate, the sound of the phonemes now activate the motor programs the child has associated with similar sounding phonemes during his babbling and the child can now both repeat the word overtly, which is important for learning to speak (and makes Dady very proud), but also rehearse it internally, as Liberman's motor theory of speech requires. There might therefore be no need for evolution to determine what motor neurons in the brain will respond to what speech sounds. Imbuing emerging human babies with an urge to play around with their vocal tract might be enough. The rest is just the result of the simple learning that even Pavlov's dog was capable of.

FOUNDATION #3: ASSOCIATING MEANING AND WORDS

In our evolutionary scenario, the emerging humans first learn to use onomatopoeia, then arbitrary words. Babbling may train their brain to echo these words, but it doesn't explain how the brain associates them with meanings? Unless all members of a community associate precisely the same meaning with the words they use, communication breaks down. Again, mirror neurons shed light onto how the brain might have come to have this capacity.

For onomatopoeia, such as "crack" or "roar," associating meaning might be particularly easy in a brain that has mirror neurons. If you have already broken objects and heard the "crack" noise that goes with doing it, your auditory mirror neurons will already associate the sound of the action with the action itself, just as Pavlov's dog associated the sound of the bell with food. If you now hear a similar sounding word "crack," the word may activate the motor program for cracking by simple physical resemblance to the sound the action made when you executed it in the past. You might consequently feel the urge to crack, which is what the person in front of you is trying to communicate. For words like "roar," during your babbling, you will have generated sounds that sound a little like a roaring lion. If you then hear a roaring lion, auditory mirror neurons will associate the sound and visual representation of a lion with the motor program for saying "roar."

For other words, the association is more difficult. If your take your first steps, and your parents start shouting: "Look you're walking! Walking!" the word sounds nothing like the action. According to a similar process of association, if your parents repeat the word often enough while you perform the action, the sound of the word can become associated with the motor program. The cells responding to these associations would no longer be auditory mirror neurons in the strict sense, because they do not respond to the execution of an action and the sound of the same action, but the associational mechanism would be similar. A monkey's brain that is able to associate actions with their sounds would be a good basis for learning to associate actions with the sound of words.

Indeed, there is now evidence from fMRI experiments that if you hear the word "lick," you activate the part of your premotor cortex you also use to move your mouth, if you hear the word "kick," you activate premotor representations of your foot actions, and if you hear to word "pick," you activate those for your hand actions[44]. All of these activations happen in the same regions that contain mirror neurons that respond to the sight of the same actions.

Third, we have to learn the meaning of words for things of the outside world, such as the word "spear" from our evolutionary scenario. A critical component here is what is called joined attention. If you saw me stare just over your head, you would turn around to see what I'm looking at. If you saw me point at a spear, you would look to see what I am pointing at and see the spear. Whether mirror neurons play a role in this convergence of attention is unclear, but Michael Platt and Stephen Shepherd at Duke University have recorded from neurons in the monkey brain that control eye movements. To their surprise they found that some of these neurons are not only active when the monkey moves his eyes, but also when the monkey simply sees another monkey move his, as if there were a direct, mirror-like connection between seeing eye movements and moving one's own eyes. With this type of neuron, seeing someone else move his eyes to look at an object would directly trigger you to look in the same direction, making your attentions converge on the same object of interest.

Such a mirror like mechanism for attention could drive the child to look at where the parent's attention is directed and, vice versa. We share this gaze mirroring behavior with monkeys, showing that the concept of mirroring, if extended to attention, prepares the emergent human's mind to understand that words uttered by others are linked to the object of their–and now also our —attention. The child can now associate the sound of the word "spear" with the sensory characteristics that define a spear.

A spear belongs to the special group of objects that can be manipulated, such as cups, hammers, and toys. These objects all have practical uses: a hammer serves to hammer, a spear serves to spear. In the 1980s, years before the discovery of mirror neurons, Giacomo Rizzolatti and colleagues in Parma found that some of the premotor neurons responsible for grasping also respond while the monkey sees an object for which that action is appropriate, even if the monkey was not executing the action at that moment[45]. They called these neurons "canonical neurons."

Canonical neurons differ from mirror neurons. Although both canonical and mirror neurons respond when the monkey himself manipulates objects, only canonical neurons also respond to the *sight of an object* for which that manipulation is appropriate, and only mirror neurons also respond to the *sight of someone else performing the same action.*

Canonical neurons may be particularly important in attributing meaning to objects like hammers and spears because they activate motor programs that are relevant to an object and these motor programs (e.g., hammering, throwing a spear) then imbue the object with a pragmatic meaning. These pragmatic units of knowledge are stored in a neighborhood close to mirror neurons that store the sound and the motor program for the arbitrary word. While someone looks at the spear and calls it spear, the brain of the observer therefore not only hears "spear" and sees it, but simultaneous activates the motor program for saying "spear" (because of his mirror neurons) and that for using a spear (because of his canonical neurons). The co-occurrence of four elements can link them together in a Pavlovian fashion, to fill the word with meaning.

Monkeys already have canonical and mirror neurons, but, unlike humans, they are missing the urge to refer to things. Cats have an urge to hunt and play-hunt as infants. Through this playful behavior they become accomplished hunters, making the best out of the hunting potential of their bodies.

Humans have an urge to call things by names. Two-year-old children restlessly ask their parents, "What do you call that?" This urge, combined with their urge to babble, makes sure that they learn some one thousand words in a couple of years.

Monkeys and apes, in contrast, just don't care about words. In the 1970s, psychologist Herbert Terrace of Columbia University attempted to teach language to chimps. He spent hours every day teaching a chimp he called "Nim Chimpsky" (as a pun on the famous linguist, Noam Chomsky, who stated that only humans have language) to use American Sign Language (ASL). He settled for this gestural form of language because chimps have not undergone the changes of vocal tract that allows humans to produce so many phonemes, and previous attempts to teach them to speak have been utter failures.

Over the years, Nim did learn to associate somewhere between twenty-five and one hundred and twenty-five signs (depending on the exact criterion used) with meanings. They could refer to bananas, to eating, etc. On the one hand, this result was a triumph because it provides support for our idea that the primate brain is prepared to learn language through the presence mirror and canonical neurons. However, it also evidences a fundamental motivational difference. Chimpsky was never as eager to learn words as a two year old would be, and his vocabulary stopped expanding around the point at which those of human children starts to really take off.

In short, the type of sensory-motor associations that are observed in mirror neurons and canonical neurons in the monkey could form the basis for Foundation #3: learning what words mean. The fact that monkeys have such associations in their auditory mirror neurons and canonical neurons shows that their brain is already capable of these associations. Why primates do not use this gift to learn language remains poorly understood, but motivational factors might be important.

FOUNDATION #4: THE GRAMMAR OF ACTIONS

Let's turn to the final step of our evolutionary scenario: the emergence of grammar. Grammar is the most peculiar feature of human language. Although Nim Chimpsky managed to learn how to associate words with meaning, what no ape has ever mastered, is grammar.

For humans, the same set of words can have a very different meaning based on their order. "Dog bites man," is no news, but "man bites dog," is. Nim never got that far. For him, "Banana Nim eat" and "Nim eat banana" was the same good news. The chimp's inability to comprehend word order stands in stark contrast to the deaf children in Nicaragua, who spontaneously invented a grammar without relevant training. Not only is there no example of other primates spontaneously using grammar, but even with intensive training, our closest living relatives, the chimpanzees, are incapable of acquiring grammar. How, then, could grammar evolve?

Let's have a brief look at what grammar really entails[iii]. Grammar is the rules of structure and logic that give language meaning. In English, elements put in different sequences have different meanings (man bites dog ≠ dog bites man). Grammar also gives language hierarchical organization and recursion. A phrase is not simply a chain of words, but has a hidden structure. In a sentence like: "The handsome young man kissed the beautiful girl—passionately ," we sense that "handsome" and "man" are somehow more connected than "young" and "kissed," despite the fact that the words are equally far apart in the sentence. We therefore sense that there is a hierarchy to the phrase, in which the four words "The handsome young man" form a unit (the subject, i.e., who did the action), "kissed passionately" forms another unit (the verb, i.e., what was being done) and "the beautiful girl," a third unit (the object, i.e., to whom it is being done). And although "kissed" and "passionately" are far away, we feel that they actually belong together.

If I now tell you that the man had actually kissed another girl the day before, you can plug this entire sentence within the above sentence, making its hierarchy recursive: "The handsome young boy, that had kissed another beautiful girl yesterday, kissed this beautiful girl today – passionately." We can embed sentences into sentences and so on, without limits.

Although the concepts of order and hidden hierarchy may be unique to humans *in the context of language*, I would argue that they are not uniquely human in general. There is one domain, in which every primate routinely masters these concepts: actions. Take eating, for instance. The basic motor program may be: reach for the berry, grasp the berry, bring it to your mouth, take your fingers out of your mouth, chew the berry. This construction by itself is already highly hierarchical, because each element is a tree of motor commands in itself (reaching for the berry involves the coordinated action of many muscles, and the way in which it will be performed is never equal, depending on how the berry is shaped, whether there are branches to avoid between me and the berry etc.), but the whole structure can become recursive if the berry is transformed into a banana. Now after grasping the banana, and before bringing it to the mouth, the chimp will use the other hand to grasp the peel of the banana, tear one lobe of the peel open, then reach for the tip again, tear that one open until the whole peel is gone, and now he continues with the original plan of bringing it to the mouth, etc. A bit like the sentence "I ate the banana" can be recursively extended into "I ate the banana I had pealed," chimpanzee action plans can therefore be recursively extended by other action plans. Just as language combines a limited vocabulary of words into an infinite number of different hierarchical phrases, primates organize a limited vocabulary of actions (grasping, reaching, tearing, etc.) into an infinite number of hierarchical action plans.

I would therefore argue that it is no mystery why the part of the premotor cortex that controls grammar is the same part of the brain that prepares our motor actions. Grammar, it seems, relies on the part of the brain that, in apes and monkeys, coordinates hierarchical structures: the premotor cortex. Although apes seem unable to use this machinery for language, they use it all the time to organize their deliberate actions. The premotor cortex that controls our actions therefore provides the primate brain with yet another prerequisite for the evolution of language: the grammar of actions.

CONCLUSION

From an evolutionary perspective, human language seems to come out of nowhere. With the discovery of mirror neurons, this has changed. Apes may not spontaneously use language, nor can they learn grammar even in contact with humans—but they have much of what it takes to do so.

Mirror neurons prepare apes to realize that they can communicate and share skills with others, and to decode phonemes by mapping them onto their own speech movements. Sensorimotor associations of the type observed in mirror neurons prepare them to associate sounds with meaning and the capacity for hierarchical sequence generation of the premotor cortex prepares their brains for the skills of grammar.

Mirror neurons are not language. From apes to Shakespeare, there is a lot of explaining left to do. But their discovery has made the seemingly giant and inexplicable leap of language evolution substantially smaller.

6

Sharing Emotions

Throughout our lives, there is virtually no moment in which we don't feel[46]. We do most things to seek the pleasures of reward and avoid the displeasures of punishment. Most of us study and work for eight hours or more every day in order to gain the social rewards of professional recognition and prestige, and also the monetary rewards that allow us to acquire goods and services that make our lives more pleasant.

Our feeling goes further than our personal experience and observation, though. While we watch James Bond being wakened by the tarantula, our understanding is not limited to his bodily actions—we also share his feelings. We sweat with his fear and rejoice with his victory. The feelings of the people that surround us are contagious. We cannot help but feel our mood drop in a room full of sorrow, and our spirits elevate around cheerful people. The sharing of ups and downs is what makes us feel like part of a group, linked together.

Introspectively, this emotional contagion appears to occur outside the sphere of our rational thinking. If we witness the sorrow of our wife, chances are that her bad news affects us directly and emotional contagion is rational. If we enter a meeting room and find a stranger crying, our mood is affected despite the fact that the stranger's bad news is highly unlikely to affect us directly. Sharing the affect of other individuals is deeply grounded in our human nature.

MODELS OF EMOTIONAL COMMUNICATIONS

Many models of social cognition do not directly address the issue of emotions. Within the idea of the mind as a powerful computer that can deal with any type of information, deducing the emotions of other individuals can be seen as just another form of deductive thinking based on rules. For example, if I see the corners of your mouth pointing downwards, you are in a bad mood or you are sad, and if you also move slowly, you are probably sad. These rules are directly comparable to rules about the world in general. If I turn the key of the car, and nothing happens, the battery might be dead or the gearbox may not be in P or N, and if none of the lights on the dashboard come on when I turn the key, the battery is probably dead. With such examples, explaining how we can understand and describe the emotions of others in intellectual ways is relatively easy, but it remains difficult to understand why our moods are directly affected by the feelings of the people around us.

EMOTIONAL CONTAGION AND FACIAL MIMICRY

An influential family of psychological theories has acknowledged the fact that there are at least two special mechanisms involved in processing the emotions of other individuals. One mechanism, called *direct facial mimicry*, was deduced from the observation that an observer's facial expression often mimics the facial expression of the people that she observes. For instance, if we see someone wince in pain, our face contracts as if in pain. We can then deduce the emotional state of that person by sensing the configuration of our own (mimicked) facial expression. Much scientific evidence exists that indicates that our facial muscles can be affected within a couple of hundred milliseconds by the observation of other people's expressions[47]. Experiments have shown that the same principle goes for the body as well.

The second, called *direct emotional contagion*, derives from the observation that we feel sad when sitting around sad individuals, and happy around happy individuals. Even young infants often start screaming when they witness the distress of other infants, as if they have "caught" the contagious emotions of the other infants.

Facial mimicry and emotional contagion are thought to interact intensively through the processes of feedback and expressions. The process of expression is very intuitive. If I witness your joy and become happy, my happiness will make me smile. In this process, my facial expression will resemble yours indirectly along a route mediated by my own feelings.

Feedback is a much less intuitive but intriguing process that links our facial expressions and body postures back to our emotional state. The concept of feedback can be traced back to the nineteenth century American philosopher and psychologist William James. William James was intrigued by the relationship between the body and the mind during emotions. He writes:

"Our natural way of thinking about these standard emotions is that the mental perception of some fact excites the mental affection called the emotion, and that this latter state of mind gives rise to the bodily expression. My thesis on the contrary is that the bodily changes follow directly the PERCEPTION of the exciting fact, and that our feeling of the same changes as they occur IS the emotion. Common sense says we lose our fortune, are sorry and weep; we meet a bear, are frightened and run; we are insulted by a rival, are angry and strike. The hypothesis here to be defended says that this order of sequence is incorrect, that the one mental state is not immediately induced by the other, that the bodily manifestations must first be interposed between, and that the more rational statement is that we feel sorry because we cry, angry because we strike, afraid because we tremble, and not that we cry, strike, or tremble, because we are sorry, angry, or fearful, as the case may be. Without the bodily states following on the perception, the latter would be purely cognitive in form, pale, colorless, destitute of emotional warmth. We might then see the bear, and judge it best to run, receive the insult and deem it right to strike, but we could not actually feel afraid or angry"[48].

James' original thought appears to contradict our intuition, but a substantial number of experiments show that our bodily state, including our facial expression, can influence our feelings. A typical experiment connects participants to a machine that measures the activity of the various muscles in the face. They are then asked to lower their eyebrows and clench their jaws or, alternatively, asked to raise the corners of their mouth. As a result, participants shape their faces as if they were frowning or smiling, without explicit reference to emotions. When asked how they feel, participants in the latter condition report feeling happier, and those in the former condition angrier, showing that their facial expression influenced their mood. A dynamic system that causes the feelings, bodily posture and facial expression of the observer to converge with those of the sender without the necessary intervention of conscious thinking is created. The observer, by imitating the facial expression of the sender, becomes a sender himself, creating a positive feedback loop between individuals that can explain how emotions can spiral upward or downward in groups. If I smile in mimicry of your smile, my smile will induce an even bigger smile in you, and make you even happier, till we all burst out laughing.

The observer can supplement the result of these preconscious mechanisms with a variety of more conscious ones. For instance, she can introspect her own bodily feelings and consciously and deliberately ask herself "how does this make me feel?" Given that, her own body and face mimic those of the observered individual and that her own feelings have been contaged by those observed, asking herself that introspective question becomes a source of information about how the other feels. Further supplementation can be added by conscious empathic emotional imagery. Reading in an email that a friend is undergoing chemotherapy may not directly lead to emotional contagion, but one can imagine what it feels like by remembering an experience of food poisoning with nausea and vomiting, which will affect our feelings. Based on reading a book by Rogers a psychologist may try to deliberately imitate the bodily posture of a patient, and this voluntary imitation will influence both his bodily posture and his feelings[49].

Conscious thought can also modulate facial mimicry and emotional contagion. Knowing that one is in competition against another individual has been shown to reduce both emotional contagion and facial mimicry. Experiments in which participants were asked to exaggerate or suppress facial expressions have also shown that this results in augmented or suppressed emotional experiences.

Through these various mechanisms, the feelings of individuals are thought to converge. But what processes actually happen in our brain when we witness the emotions of other individuals? The mirror neuron system transforms actions we observe into a motor representation of similar actions. Could facial mimicry and emotional contagion be explained by the presence of similar neurons in regions involved in our facial expressions or emotional feelings?

SHARING THE FEELING OF DISGUST

July 17, 2002, Marseille: A strange smell comes out of Jean-Pierre Royet's Renault Espace—something halfway between banana skins and rotten eggs. My friend Bruno Wicker and I help him move boxes full of plastic bottles into the little building next to the hospital where an fMRI scanner is located. "Qu'est-ce qui pue comme ça?" the fMRI technician asks us in French. "What stinks so much?"

Royet grins at me. Almost a year earlier, my colleague Bruno and I sat in this city on a wall overlooking the Mediterranean, conceiving an experiment to test for emotional mirror neurons. We did our PhDs together in St. Andrews, but I had moved to Parma to continue working with monkeys, and Bruno had moved to Marseille to concentrate on fMRI studies with human participants, and emotions have been at the center of his interest. Having become interested in emotions too, and given that we did not have an fMRI scanner in Parma, I thought I might visit Bruno in Marseille.

"What we would need," I had told Bruno on that sunny afternoon, "is an experiment in which we place a participant in the scanner, evoke an emotion to measure the brain areas involved in experiencing the emotion, and also show the same participant the emotions of others to discover if seeing the emotion activates parts of the circuit involved in experiencing the emotion."

"I couldn't agree more," Bruno replied, clearly having thought exactly the same thing. "We have two problems though. First, finding at least two emotions that have different patterns of brain activity, and second, finding a way to trigger these emotions in the scanner."

He was right. To test for the presence of specific mirroring using fMRI, we needed at least *two* emotions that cause distinguishable brain activity. When testing the auditory mirror system, we had shown it to be selective because the sound of hand actions activated areas involved in the execution of hand actions, and the sound of mouth actions activated areas involved in the execution of mouth actions.

Unfortunately, most emotions are very difficult to trigger in a scanner environment. For emotions such as happiness, fear, or sadness, we could not conceive of any way to repeatedly trigger the emotion in the scanner. After some thought, we agreed that disgust is the best emotion to use for such an experiment. "I know a researcher, Royet, who is a specialist in olfaction. I think he has a device for presenting smells in a controlled manner in the scanner. We could present unpleasant odors that would trigger a feeling of disgust, and contrast those with pleasant odors."

So, to answer the lab technician's question, what stinks is the key to triggering emotions in the scanner: little plastic bottles containing cotton swabs dipped into various substances that we perceive as odors. Some containe pleasant smells like strawberry or mint, others, causing us so much discomfort, are substances like butyric acid or furfuryl mercaptan that smell like rancid butter and rotten eggs respectively.

Valeria is our first guinea-pig. Royet straps an anesthesia mask onto her mouth, and the technician moves her into the scanner. At first, she sees a series of movies with actors sniffing the contents of a glass. In some, the actor show no particular reaction. These are our neutral movies. In others, the actor makes a disgusted facial expression, wrinkling his nose, and moving away from the glass quickly. In the last type of movie, the actor raises one of his eyebrows and expresses a subtle smile of appreciation, as if agreeing that this was a good wine indeed. Then, Valeria finds out why she has the anesthesia mask on her face. Royet squeezes the contents of various bottles into a rubber-tubing that leads to the anesthesia mask, and the repulsive smells of rotten eggs or rancid butter, or the relatively pleasant scents of strawberry and mint, make Valeria experience the same emotional roller coaster the actors had experienced in the movies.

In this experiment, the pleasant odors and the movies showing pleased actors are not as intensely positive as the negative ones, negative. Such a result was inevitable because positive emotions in response to the contents of a glass will never be as strong as negative emotions can be under the same circumstances. Examples of strongly positive olfactory experiences do exist–for instance, shortly after falling in love, the perfume of our loved one can make us feel ecstatic–but the intensely positive emotions we feel in those cases are not directly caused by the odor, but are due to emotional experiences we associate with the odors. Odors per se have the power to trigger intense disgust, but only moderate pleasure. Our main focus is therefore to find regions that would respond to the experience and observation of disgust, which is intense in both the olfactory and the visual conditions, and show that these regions are less active for positive emotions, which would serve as a control condition.

After a series of pleasant and unpleasant odors, the experiment is finished. "Some of those smells were terrible!" Valeria sais. "I almost started retching at one point." The olfactory part has clearly worked.

After running this procedure with a dozen participants, we examined the data. During the olfactory part of the experiment, only the unpleasant odors had strongly activated a region called the anterior insula on both sides of the brain. The insula is a part of the brain that receives input from both our nose and tongue, and processes the tastes and flavors of food. In the monkey, it contains neurons that are activated by certain bad tastes and smells, and also receives input from the internal organs, so it makes sense that it is activated by the bad odors and the bodily sensations that go with them. These bodily sensations in particular should be much smaller for the pleasant odors that should, accordingly, activate the insula less - exactly what we found.

Surgeons have studied what people feel when their insula is activated. When the neurosurgeon Wilder Penfield electro-stimulated the insula of his epileptic patients, they reported feeling unpleasant sensations in their throat, and some even started retching[50]. He had also put a pressure-sensitive balloon in the patients' stomachs, and showed that the electro-stimulation also caused movements of the stomach. Activations in the insula thus appear to go hand-in-hand with our bodily, visceral sense of nausea. The activations in the insula we could measure in our experiment were thus the neural correlate of Valeria feeling intense bodily disgust while smelling the unpleasant odors.

But what happened while our subjects viewed the emotions of others? While watching the movies of facial expressions, the visual and premotor areas of the mirror system that would be involved in making similar facial expressions were activated as if our subjects automatically mimicked, in the brain, the facial expressions they observed. Now, if there is a mirror system for emotions, the anterior insula, which is specific for the experience of the disgusting smells, should also have been activated, making participants feel disgusted themselves. Our data analysis showed that this is exactly what happened[51].

We were delighted. Over a decade after the discovery of mirror neurons in the motor system, we had provided the first evidence that a similar system exists outside the domain of actions. We had unraveled what in the brain causes what the psychologists call facial mimicry, vicarious activity in the premotor cortex as if doing the same facial expressions, and what they call emotional contagion, vicarious activity in the insula as if feeling the same emotions.

FROM MIRROR NEURONS TO SHARED CIRCUITS

The term mirror neuron had been coined in the context of actions because, through mirror neurons, the brain internally simulates the actions of other people and generates a mirror image of their actions. Now we had discovered a similar system for emotions, and so we needed a new term to describe this system—mirror neurons were just too tied to the motor system. Just as the premotor cortex shared two processes, executing actions and seeing/hearing other individuals perform similar actions, the insula appeared to share two emotional processes of experiencing the strong bodily feeling of disgust and seeing disgust in other individuals. Both the premotor cortex and the insula are involved in neural circuits that allow us to vicariously share the actions and emotions of other individuals. We coined the term "shared circuits" to describe this whole family of neural processes, including mirror neurons for actions, and similar systems including the insula for disgust[52, 53].

RECOGNIZING EMOTION IN OTHERS

In our experiment, we showed that the insula is activated while participants look at the disgusted facial expressions of other people, which suggests that this area is involved in perceiving the facial expressions of others by transforming the seen emotions into a representation of our own emotions. Is this simulation the reason we understand the emotions of other people?

We cannot answer this question using fMRI alone, because it cannot disentangle cause and effect. The brake lights of your car, for instance, light up each time you press the brakes and the car then decelerates. In our experiment, the same sort of thing happened with the insula. It became active when the participants saw a disgusted facial expression and then recognized that the person was disgusted. Can we conclude from those observations that the brake lights of your car are what make your car decelerate? Can we conclude that the activity in the insula following the sight of disgusted facial expressions makes you understand that the person is disgusted? For the car example, there is a relatively simple experimental method for testing the causal link between the brake lights and deceleration: take a hammer, smash the brake lights, and see if the car still decelerates. If it does, the brake lights were not necessary for slowing the car down. If it stops decelerating, they were.

In humans, a way to follow a similar line of thinking is to examine patients who have experienced brain damage because of trauma, disease, or strokes in the area being investigated. Testing such patients allows scientists to examine whether damage to a particular brain area interferes with a particular brain function.

In 2000, Andy Calder and his colleagues in Cambridge, England, reported examining a twenty-five year old man, known as NK, who had suffered from a stroke that damaged his left insula[54]. First, Andy showed NK photos of unfamiliar people taken from different perspectives and asked him to indicate those that were from the same individual. NK performed normally at this test. NK also recognized photos of famous people. His capacity to perceive faces was preserved.

Andy then tested him on emotional facial expressions. He showed NK photos of happy, surprised, afraid, angry, sad, and disgusted faces. For each picture, NK had a choice of six basic emotional words and had to select the one that fitted the face best. When NK was shown happy faces, he swiftly chose the label "happy." When shown a surprised face, he selected "surprised." He also responded normally to afraid, angry, and sad faces. Yet, when Andy showed NK a photo of a disgusted face, NK was puzzled, and after a pause decided in half the cases that the person was angry rather than disgusted. Andy also asked sixty healthy individuals to do the same task, and they recognized disgust in over 80 percent of the cases. NK was selectively impaired in understanding that a person was disgusted from looking at facial expressions.

The insula thus appears to be *necessary* for recognizing disgust in others, whereas brake lights are not necessary for slowing down a car. Note that the deficit was restricted to disgust, a fact that fits with the findings from the fMRI study because the sight of the pleased faces did not activate the insula as much as the disgusted faces. Other brain areas are probably necessary for recognizing these other emotions.

RECOGNIZING EMOTIONAL SOUNDS

Testing other modalities, such as sounds and vocal intonation produced the same results, suggesting that the insula region we had identified not only transforms an observed facial expression of disgust into the observer's experience of disgust, but also transforms the sound of disgust into a similar experience–much as motor mirror neurons respond to both the sound and the sight of actions.

That the same brain region is necessary for seeing and hearing disgust in others is of importance. Shared circuits seem to be generally sensitive to evidence of other people's actions and emotions, independent of whether this evidence is seen or heard. We have all experienced how a sob and a tone of voice in a phone call can make us share the emotions of a partner as strongly and vigorously as having the person in front of us. The fact that shared circuits are multimodal helps us understand these phenomena. For the brain, different sensory evidence is transformed into a single token of social cognition–our own experience of similar actions and feelings. Differences between phone calls and encounters are then more quantitative than qualitative, because in a physical encounter, evidence from visual, auditory, and tactile senses can add together to form a more intense sharing in face to face situations, but sounds can trigger a similar, albeit sometimes weaker, sharing through the very same mechanisms.

YOU NEED TO FEEL EMOTIONS TO EMPATHIZE WITH OTHERS

Central to our idea of a shared circuit for disgust is not just the fact that the insula is involved in recognizing disgust in others, but also the notion that the insula is also required for experiencing disgust oneself. In accordance with this theory, we expect that the lesion in NK's insula should also have impaired his own experience of disgust.

As a final experiment, Andy gave NK a number of scales that measured the strength of his experience of emotions. When asked about his experience of fear or anger, his answers indicated that he had a normal experience of them. Then he was asked to indicate how disgusted he would be in a number of situations. For example, one of the questions on the scale asks how disgusted you would be if you go to a public toilet, find that the person before you had diarrhea, and sprayed all over the toilet seat and wall, creating a very foul smell. Here NK indicated that he would not be disgusted at all. His sense of disgust was clearly reduced.

Intrigued by this finding, Andy wondered if NK even knew what disgust was, and asked him to produce scenarios in which other people would be disgusted. NK effortlessly produced plausible scenarios show that, though he knew what disgust was at a conceptual level, his own propensity to experience and recognize it was impaired. An intellectual understanding is not enough to understand our social world: our intuitions are essential.

Ralph Adolphs and his colleagues in Iowa, some four thousand miles away described a strikingly similar patient[55]. This patient, named "Mr. B," had suffered from a brain infection, Herpes Simplex. His damage, which was much more extensive than that of NK, included vast areas of the brain in addition to the insula. As a result, he was deeply amnesic and unable to make new memories. Each time they met, Ralph had to remind Mr. B of who he was.

Ralph tested Mr. B extensively regarding his capacity to experience and observe disgust. The results were the same as Andy's with NK. Mr. B's abilities to recognize or consciously experience disgust were greatly reduced. Ralph went further in his examination of the nature of Mr. B's gustatory experience of disgust[56]. He gave Mr. B two different drinks, one of salt water, and one of sugar, and asked Mr. B to try both. Mr. B tried the sugar solution, looked pleased, and said it was delicious. He then tried the salty solution, smiled and said it was delicious. Mr. B's lack of conscious appreciation of gustatory unpleasantness is in line with the idea that the insula is critical for the processing of disgusting tastes and smells.

Next, Ralph added some food color to the drinks, making the salt solution red and the sugar solution green. Mr. B had to try both solutions, and then decide which one he wanted to continue drinking. Although Mr. B showed a pleased facial expression after trying both, he always decided to continue drinking the green, sugar solution. Ralph then asked him if he wanted to try to red (salt) solution again, and Mr. B vehemently refused. Ralph asked Mr. B to describe both solutions, and Mr. B told him, they both tasted like "pop," showing no conscious awareness of a difference between the two drinks.

Experiments such as those done on NK and Mr. B helps us understand how the insula contributes to our own sense of disgust. Without an insula, Mr. B's brain still knew what was good for him and what was not, making him choose the sugar solution over the salt solution. What Mr. B's brain no longer did was give him a "conscious feeling state" of disgust while he drank the salt solution. By conscious feeling state, we mean a state in which you are conscious of feeling something. In the brain, processing what is bad and consciously feeling nausea and disgust can be two different things. The insula is essential for creating the latter but not the former, as shown by Mr. B's preserved capacity to choose the better, sugar solution over the salt solution, even without an insula, but without consciously knowing why.

CONNECTING WHAT YOU SEE WITH WHAT YOU FEEL

A detective deciding whether or not a suspect is guilty sometimes looks through the phone calls that the suspect has made. Seeing with whom the suspect is connected gives insight into the role he may have had in the crime. Neuroscientists often do the same. Knowing the connections of an area allows us to examine whether that area receives the right type of information to perform a certain function and whether it can send information to the right brain areas to take the necessary actions.

Two American anatomists, Marsel Mesulam and Elliott Mufson at Harvard University, examined the connections of the insula by injecting dies that mark the pathways of its incoming and outgoing connections[57]. The anterior insula, which our fMRI experiment showed to be active in the observation and experience of disgust, receives input from brain regions that process information from all the bodily senses, as well as input from nerves that sense the inner state of our bodily organs including the heart, intenstine and stomach. That information is then sent back as a motor command to the same visceral organs and the hypothalamus to change our bodily state, for instance, by making us retch if we had eaten something bad or by triggering the release of stress hormones to prepare us for danger.

The pattern of connections described above has two important implications for the function of the insula. First, capable of sensing the inner state of our body, the insula can read our "gut feelings." Such a gut feeling is central to bodily states associated with food, like nausea. Without the capacity to sense their inner states, NK and Mr. B appeared to stop feeling disgust. Their brains may still process that a taste is good or bad for the body, subconsciously, but they lost the feeling of being "sick to their stomach" that is so important to our diagnosis of disgust.

Second, the convergence of visual and auditory input to the insula allows it to link signals about the disgust of others to the neurons that read our body's own disgust. This convergence might be the key to the activation of the insula both during the experience and observation of disgust in our fMRI experiment. Without that convergence, Mr. B and NK were unable to relate the feeling of disgust of others to their own feeling of nausea. Without this feeling, disgust stops really being disgust.

THE BODY IS PART AND PARCEL OF THE MIND

We often think of our mind as being detached from our body. In the age of computers, science fiction writers dream of an eternal life of the mind, stored in a computer. As a kid, I was fascinated by that idea. Each time I had a cold, or toothache, I wondered how nice life would be if we were relieved of the aches and pains of our imperfect bodies.

But there is much more to us than our conscious logical mind. The patients Mr. B and NK epitomize how a life deprived of the feelings of our own body is incomplete. By losing the connection between mind and body, we lose our capacity to feel certain emotions, much as William James was proposing. Imagine how miserable would life be without the warmth that comes from a partner's embrace, how short would our lives be if damaging our bodies didn't feel so damned painful, and what love would mean without the sense of physical pain we feel while we are far away from the people that are dear to us.

Even if our logical thinking is sometimes clouded by our emotions, without the physical feeling of thrill we sense when our thinking leads to success, I doubt we would care to think at all. Our mind is grounded in our bodies. Through the discovery of shared circuits, the body becomes central not only to our own emotional lives but also to the exchanges between our minds. To understand the actions of other individuals, we need to map them onto our own body's motor programs. To understand their emotions, we need to map them onto our own visceral feelings. The Hollywood characters of the Vulcan Captain Spock or the Android Data in Star Trek epitomize how much flatter our lives would be without the ups and downs of our bodily emotions. The fascination these characters have for emotions is a reflection of our own fascination with these powerful states. Their incapacity to understand what really goes on in the emotion-driven human beings that surround them is a testimony to how important our emotions are as a key to those of others. It takes one to know one. . .

The body is critical for this mapping, and the insula appears to be part of a process in which the conscious mind becomes aware of the result of this bodily mapping. We have to stop thinking in dualistic terms that asset the conscious logical rational mind in opposition against gut reactions. The body, brain, and conscious mind are partners, in permanent exchange. Many of the important processes for social cognition in particular occur inside the brain but outside the conscious mind.

MORE EMPATHIC PEOPLE ACTIVATE THE INSULA MORE STRONGLY

Earlier we determined that more empathic individuals activate their own actions more strongly than less empathic individuals while watching the actions of others. It follows that their own emotions should be activated more strongly while observing the emotions of others. In 2007, together with Mbemba Jabbi, a good-humored PhD student of mine that had come to the Netherlands as a refugee from the civil war in Sierra Leone, we addressed this question. Fascinated by emotions, Mbemba scanned eighteen participants using a similar experiment to the one I had conducted with Bruno Wicker, but showing movies of disgusted and neutral facial expressions. Instead of the weakly appreciative facial expression movies Bruno and I had used, Mbemba asked his actors to look ecstatic after trying the contents of a cup, as if they had been very thirsty and were intensely refreshed by the delicious contents. He then showed these movie clips to participants while measuring their brain activity with fMRI. Later, he had the participants taste pleasant and unpleasant substances in the scanner. Most importantly, inspired by the pioneering work of the German neuroscientist Tania Singer, he asked the participants to fill out Davis's empathy questionnaire (see Appendix 1) so he could measure if empathic individuals indeed activate regions involved in their own gustatory experiences more strongly while viewing the emotions of other individuals[58].

What excited Mbemba the most was the fact that the more empathic a participant reported to be in life, based on the Davis questionnaire, the more strongly he activated his own visceral sensations in the insula during the sight of other people's emotions[59]. This provided strong support for the idea that what we were measuring in the insula was indeed the neural process that underlies our feeling of sharing emotions with others, as measured by the questionnaire.

These inter-individual differences in how strongly people share the feelings of others may be at the heart of why different people react very differently to movies. Some of us cry during a sad movie, and others remain untouched. Some enjoy horror movies, while others literally feel sick at the sight of a person being decapitated with an ax. Empathic people activate their insula very strongly and may be overwhelmed by the vicarious emotions that movies trigger in them. Other people may activate their insula only weakly, needing much stronger stimuli to trigger their own feelings.

As with actions, the question of what causes these differences remains. More empathic people may either watch emotions more attentively, or look at the images with the same attention, but have stronger connections between the visual and auditory areas processing the display of emotions and their own feelings in the insula.

DELIGHT IS ALSO SHARED IN THE INSULA

Our first fMRI study had focused on the negative emotion of disgust because we believed we could trigger this emotion better than positive emotions. Fortunately, life also allows us to share and understand the joys and pleasures of other individuals. The sounds of relish and facial expressions of delight we sometimes deliberately produce to trigger a child's interest in food demonstrates how intuitively aware we are of being attuned to other people's pleasure. In Mbemba's study, we deliberately made the facial displays of pleasure intense, to check if they would also trigger the representation of bodily feelings, which indeed turned out to be the case. The insula was activated by the sight of pleasure in the same location as during the displays of disgust, suggesting that both unpleasant and pleasant bodily representations can be triggered by the view of facial expressions. These representations of delight were also more strongly activated in more empathic individuals.

If the insula causes us to share both pleasant and unpleasant sensations, why do patients with lesions in the area have problems only with disgust and not with positive emotions? A facial expression of disgust is strongly indicative of the kind of visceral feelings the insula seems to process. A smile, however, *can* but does not have to signal visceral feelings. For example, when we politely smile at colleagues each morning, there is no sense of intense pleasure. Our feeling of disgust is therefore most strongly impaired because it depends heavily on visceral sensations. Although visceral sensations can be a source of happiness, happiness in general does not depend on visceral sensations in the way disgust does. To draw an analogy, the insula is more essential for disgust than happiness, just as your sense of coldness is more essential to recognizing that ice cream is ice cream but not to recognize that orange juice is orange juice–despite the fact that a ice cream and a cold glass of orange juice can activate your sense of coldness equally strongly. Our understanding of happiness can rely on other, non-visceral components –just as coldness can be a part of our experience of a good glass of orange juice, but our capacity to recognize orange juice would not be impaired by a loss of the sense of coldness. Nevertheless, visceral sensations can be a source of happiness, especially when it is related to foods, and this is what Mbemba appeared to pick up.

With this series of experiments, we took an important step closer to discovering how we understand other people. When we witness the actions and emotions of others, our brain makes us share these actions and emotions, by activating parts of the brain that are normally part of performing the same actions or experiencing the same emotions. Although this principle had first been observed for actions, it now became clear that it was more general. Emotions appear to obey the very same principle–I can feel what you feel.

THE POWER OF WORDS

We have all experienced how moving a good novel can be. Compared to seeing what other people do and feel, which animals have done for millions of years, writing is a new invention, no more than ten thousand years old. How the brain deals with this new invention to make us feel so moved by a novel is a question Mbemba and I tried to address. Specifically, we wanted to know whether written stories could somehow plug into the same brain region as the sight of other people's emotions. We measured brain activity in the same people that had seen and felt disgust and pleasure in our previous experiment, but this time we gave them little scenario's to read. One of them read: "When you turn around to look who is leaning on your shoulder, you are peering into the unsightly face of a homeless guy. When you try to free yourself from his penetrating presence, you briefly see a glance of his rotten teeth that are circled with bad sores before his eyes start to roll. The guy leans forward and discharges the complete content of his inflamed stomach on you! You are covered with decaying vomit that was formed by rotten meat picked out of the garbage cans across the street. It has been a long time since you have felt this sick. You can feel your stomach contract. Then you feel a hard, fleshy piece of his vomit in the corner of your mouth…" We directly measured activity in the part of the insula that we had previously found to be active both while they viewed the disgusted facial expressions of others and while they experienced bad tastes themselves. To our amazement, the same region became strongly activated while people read such disgusting scenario, and much so then when they read an emotionaly neutral story[26]. We then used a technique called psychophysiological interaction to examine which brain regions may have been responsible for triggering the activity in the insula while reading the stories or while viewing the disgusted facial expressions of others. Although the insula was similarly active in both cases, it turned out that it had been triggered by different brain regions in the two cases. While viewing the facial expressions of others, it was triggered by the premotor cortex that mirrors the facial expressions that had been observed. While reading, it was triggered by regions known to process language, such as Broca's area and the temporal pole. The insula therefore seemed to be a common arena for our own emotions, those we see in others and those we read about. There, our own actual emotions come together with those of others and those we read about and imagine. The brain somehow flexibly directs the various forms of information to this same, shared insula, whether the information is the evolutionary older, face-to-face view or the newer, written information. The mechanism of activating a region that is responsible for your own emotions while witnessing those of others was even more general than we originally thought.

IT TAKES ONE TO KNOW ONE

Common wisdom often assumes that empathy is an undividable trait, that a person is either more or less empathic. When we describe the personality of other individuals, we seldom specify domains of empathy. Our experiments seemed to suggest that we should.

In both our experiments on the sound of actions and facial expressions, we had observed that participants with higher empathy scores activated either their premotor or their insular cortex, depending on the experiment, more strongly. A closer examination of Davis's scale makes it clear that different aspects of the empathy scale correlate with premotor and insular activity[14]. When listening to the sound of *actions,* the activity in the premotor cortex was stronger in individuals that scored high in the "Perspective Taking" subscale of the questionnaire. The subscale contains statements such as: "I sometimes try to understand my friends better by imagining how things look from their perspective." On the other hand, the activity in the insula while people observe *emotions* correlated with more emotional subscales of empathy, specifically the "Personal Distress" and "Fantasy" scales. Participants who agreed with the statement: "I sometimes feel helpless when I am in the middle of a very emotional situation," would therefore activate their own visceral sensations in the insula more than others. Notably, the correlation between the perspective taking scale, on the one hand, and the personal distress and fantasy scales, on the other, was low, indicating that participants that engage in a lot of "Perspective Taking" are not necessarily the same as those that are upset by the distress of other individuals.

The fact that two brain areas involved in different aspects of understanding other individuals correlate with different subscales means that we should not think of empathy or understanding other people as a single phenomenon. Premotor areas mirror the *actions* of other people, and may enable us to perceive other individuals' goals and motivations from their perspective. The insula on the other hand mirrors the *visceral state* of other people, and may enable us to share their emotions. In life, these two components often interact and contribute to a comprehensive intuitive feel for the inner lives of the people that surround us, including both their goals and emotions, but this capacity can be split into somewhat separable components. Some people appear to be particularly good at mirroring the actions, others at mirroring the emotions of other people, and some are particularly good at both or neither. Empathy should thus be seen as a mosaic of subcomponents that together build up the final image of what goes on in other people.

As it turns out, the subdivisions of our empathy have an even finer grain because the differences in our personal experiences will determine the differences in our empathy. Those of us who often suffer from sinus pain, like me, are exquisitely empathic for other people's sinus pain–but much less for back pain.

THE DIFFERENCE BETWEEN A FAKE AND A REAL SMILE

So far we have shown that the insula is involved in sharing the visceral emotions of other individuals, such as disgust or food-related pleasure. If our brain deduces these visceral states from other people's emotional facial expressions and behavior, then the insula must somehow receive input from regions that process this observable motor behavior. In the light of the discovery of mirror neurons, one might suspect that regions controlling facial expressions might be involved in this process.

Looking at the smile of a politician, we immediately sense that it is fake. The corners of their mouth are pointing upwards, but the region surrounding their eyes is relaxed. Faking a smile is notoriously difficult. Actors, who fake facial expressions for a living, do not generally try to fake a smile–they do their best to enter a cheerful state of mind, and the smile then comes naturally.

Why are facial expressions so hard to create on purpose? The answer lies in the fact that the brain areas that control the voluntary movement of your face are different from those that cause the emotional generation of facial expressions[60]. The premotor cortex and primary motor cortex we encountered in the previous chapters are part of the voluntary motor system. If you fake a smile without generating the emotion, you use these two cortical areas. I term this system the "cold" facial expression system, because it does not require the heat of emotions. The cold system also controls your facial motor program for masticating, blowing your nose, articulating, and the other goal directed behavior we produce using our face.

In parallel to this system, regions in the midline between the two hemispheres of your brain, around the cingulate sulcus, produce involuntary emotional behavior. The wrinkling of your nose when you smell something foul, the contraction of your face when you feel pain, and the laughter when you hear something funny, are all controlled by these midline motor structures. I call this system the "hot" motor system, because it transforms the heat of emotional affect into observable behavior of the face and the body.

The hot and cold facial motor systems send their output directly to the nucleus in the base of the brain that controls the muscles in the face—they converge onto the same muscles but have independent representations of motor programs. The fact that the hot and cold motor programs are stored in separate cortical locations means that we cannot willingly activate the emotional smile motor program. If we want to fake a smile, we have to create a new motor program that deliberately reproduces the sequence of muscle movements used by the hot motor program, and the result will always look like a poor reproduction.

The independence of the hot and cold facial control system becomes very apparent after certain lesions. Lesions affecting the cold motor control system leave people unable to deliberately move their faces. If you tell such a patient a good joke, he will laugh and smile although he is unable to fake a smile or deliberately move his face. The opposite is true after lesions to the hot motor control system. These patients are able to move their faces deliberately, but their faces will not move during their experience of emotions.

If we have two motor systems that control our faces, what happens to them when we view the facial expressions of others? I exampined this question with my friend Christiaan van der Gaag[61].

We used fMRI to measure participants' brain activity while they watched short movie clips of an actor laughing, looking disgusted, and looking afraid. We then asked the participants to make certain facial expressions as they lay in the scanner, and asked them to place themselves in the mood of the target emotion so that they would activate both the hot and the cold motor control systems. If participants have a mirror system for facial expressions, parts of the hot and/or cold motor system should be activated by the sight of the facial expressions of other individuals. We found that, as expected, the observation of all of these facial expressions activated a circuit that was also active when participants were asked to make similar facial expressions. This shared circuit for the observation and execution of facial expressions involved three main regions: the temporal cortex, which provides a visual description of the observed facial expressions; the premotor cortex, which is part of the cold motor control system; and regions along the cingulate sulcus that are part of the hot motor cortex.

The cold part of this shared circuit resembled what Valeria had found to be active both during the sound and the execution of mouth actions[9]. Both included regions of the temporal lobe and the premotor cortex. At the same time, viewing facial expressions also activated the hot motor control system in the midline of the brain. The activation was stronger for emotional facial expressions compared to the observation of movements of the face that carried no emotional content.

Importantly, the primary motor cortex, which sends the strongest and most direct connections to the facial muscles, was active only while participants executed facial expressions but not while they observed other people's facial expressions.

When we look at facial expressions, we must activate both a neural representation of similar feelings in our insula and of a similar facial expression in our cold and hot motor cortex. These findings have brought the revolution set in motion by mirror neurons yet a step further. It turns out that, as we observe the behavior of other individuals, our brain appears to share a rich mosaic of neural activity with the observed individual, including representations of his bodily actions, his feelings, and his facial expressions.

SHARING FACIAL EXPRESSIONS IS ESSENTIAL FOR UNDERSTANDING OTHERS' EMOTIONS

Ralph Adolphs and his colleagues in Iowa have examined a large number of people with localized brain damage[62]. The individuals had suffered strokes or other forms of brain injury and agreed to participate in psychological experiments. They were shown a number of different photographs of faces showing emotional expressions and were then asked to rate the photos according to how angry the person was, how fearful, how happy, and so on. The researchers observed that only a certain proportion of the patients had problems identifying the emotions of other people from their facial expressions. They compared the location of the brain damage in these impaired participants with the location of the damage in the participants that had no trouble in recognizing emotions. It turned out that those with problems seemed to have lesions in the premotor cortex of the right hemisphere, exactly where Christiaan van der Gaag had found activity while participants viewed and executed facial expressions. Thus, damage to the cold facial motor system seems to lead to deficits in recognizing facial expressions. While we observe the facial expression of other individuals, being able to simulate internally what their face does seems important for understanding their inner states.

FACIAL MIMICRY TRIGGERS EMOTIONAL CONTAGION

Emotions and the motor system are linked in many ways. For instance, which pair of letters do you like more: FV or FJ? As it turns out, your answer depends on how much time you spend behind a keyboard. If you use keyboards a lot, you probably like FJ better than FV for the simple reason that FJ can be typed more easily because it uses fingers from different hands[63]. Although most people showing this preference are unaware of the true reason for their preference, their motor system thus determines their emotional preference. People that do not use keyboards much do not have that preference.

With Mbemba Jabbi, we explored whether there is a link between the activation in the cold motor control system and the activation of feelings in the insula for facial expressions. When participants viewed movies of facial expressions, their activity in the insula and premotor cortex was not always the same. In some trials, the disgusted faces activated the insula more strongly, in others more weakly. The same happened with premotor facial programs. If the sharing of facial movements in the cold motor system operated independent of the sharing of emotions in the insula, the trials in which the insula was more active would not necessarily be the trials where the cold motor system would respond more strongly. If, on the other hand, they are connected, strong insula trials should also be strong cold motor control trials.

Mbemba found that when people observed neutral facial movements, such as someone drinking through a straw, there was no link between the insula and the cold motor system. When people viewed disgusted or pleased facial expressions on the other hand the two systems were linked. Whenever the premotor cortex had strongly activated facial programs, the insula had strongly activated visceral feelings. Interestingly, activations in the premotor cortex predicted those in the insula more than the other way around, suggesting that our brain first simulates what the other person's face is doing in the premotor cortex, and once you share the facial expression in your premotor cortex, your insula kicks in, making you share the feelings of that person[64].

SHARING EMOTIONS WITH A POKER-FACE

The brain appears to simulate the movements of the face through the cold motor system whether the movement is emotional or not. If the facial expression signals a bodily emotion such as disgust or pleasure, information is exchanged between the premotor cortex and the insula, triggering a representation of similar visceral feelings. We now not only feel what the face is doing, but also what the person is feeling inside, and we share his pleasure or his disgust. Given that the insula also receives direct input from visual areas, two routes may converge toward emotional contagion. One directly triggers the representations of feelings based on the sight of the emotional facial expression, and one does so indirectly, by first translating the visual description into a motor representation in the hot and cold facial motor control system, and then triggering the representation of corresponding feelings through connections between these motor systems and the insula.

Psychologists had previously generated quite an accurate theory of emotional communication by combining the idea of emotional contagion and facial mimicry. Looking directly into the brain confirms the interaction between activating similar feelings and reproducing similar facial expressions, but also changes the theory in two profound ways.

First, the neuroscientific evidence shows that the most strongly activated motor regions are not the primary motor cortex but higher level motor areas including the "cold" premotor cortex and the "hot" cingulate motor cortex. Whereas activity in the primary motor cortex directly leads to observable overt changes in the body, activity in these higher level areas, in the absence of primary motor cortex activity, can remain covert. Just as people can activate their premotor cortex without moving their own hands when seeing someone else grasp a ball, they can also activate these higher order motor areas when viewing facial expressions without necessarily moving their face. The observer then feels a bit as if he had made a similar facial expression without actually doing so. This process is conceptually linked to what psychologists had termed facial mimicry because it is a motor function, but differs from facial mimicry in that it does not necessarily lead to movements in the face of the observer. Depending on a number of factors, this higher level motor simulation *can* be sent to the primary motor cortex and to the facial muscles and *can* lead to the overt facial mimicry psychologists have sometimes measured as muscle activity in the face of the observer, but this process is optional. If the person in front of me is my enemy or competitor or if I want to hide my emotional involvement, my face can remain stoic, not providing any overt testimony of my motor simulation[65].

The distinction between activating a representation of similar facial expressions in higher level motor areas and overt facial mimicry explains why researchers fail to find a robust link between overt mimicry and the understanding of emotions[66]. The higher level *covert* simulation is what provides insights into the emotions of others. *Overt* facial mimicry on the other hand is nothing more or less than an *instrumental* tool in social exchanges.

Mimicry may, for instance, help to establish a bond between sender and observer, since it signals the observer's willingness to tune into the emotions of the sender. In psychological or psychiatric practice, this can be important in strengthening the patient-therapist relationship[49]. Repressing overt mimicry on the other hand can be instrumental in signaling that one does not wish to tune into the emotions of particular people. For example, not smiling in return to a smile is an effective "leave me alone" message, and not looking sad in front of a crying child an effective way to suggest to the child to "get a grip."

Both the observation of bodily actions and of facial expressions leads to activity in the premotor cortex. Both can, but do not have to, lead to overt imitation. Despite this similarity, overt mimicry is more frequent for facial expressions than for goal directed hand actions in which TMS stimulation is often needed to render the muscle activity measurable. Why this difference? The answer might be very simple. If you and I were seated in a restaurant, both dining alone on separate tables, and you smile in response to my smile after seeing a waiter accidentally pour a plate of soup over a snobbish and obnoxious client, we would feel "connected." Such facial mimicry has been shown to encourage me to interact with you more, and makes me generally think of you in more positive ways. Overtly mimicking the waiter's hand actions and pouring your own plate of soup over someone else would have much more negative effects. In general, imitating goal directed actions during observation often has negative effects because it interferes with the observer's own behavior. Facial expressions do not usually cause such interference.

BLURRING THE BORDER BETWEEN INDIVIDUALS

Our western societies are built around the individual and his right to pursue happiness. Values such as marriage, family, and nation are increasingly replaced by the individual seeking his own personal fulfillment. Elderly parents go to retirement homes so as not to infringe on their child's freedom to live as they wish. Economic theory assumes that humans are *homo economicus*, that is, rational beings that do what is best for themselves.

Neuroscience cannot tell us what the relationship between human individuals should be, or whether individualism is good or bad. All it can tell us is what our nature looks like, and how millions of years of evolution have shaped our brain to relate to other people. In doing so, the discovery of shared circuits has changed our understanding of the link between the individual mind and the people around us.

Before shared circuits, our vision of the brain was essentially individualistic. The "world out there"—including the people that surround us—was represented in sensory brain areas. The "self" and its free will were located in strictly separate brain areas. These latter "personal" brain regions dealt with the functions of the individual, such as deciding what of a number of alternatives the individual would decide to believe in or do, where attention would be focused, and which memories to store or retrieve. Of course, the world around us could influence these personal brain areas but this influence remained indirect, and strictly separable from our second to second personal individual agency. The individual had a clear border both in society and in the brain.

In light of the new research, people around us are no longer just part of "the world out there," restricted to sensory brain areas. Through shared circuits, the people around us, their actions and their emotions, permeate into many areas of our brain that were formerly the safe harbors of our identity: our motor system and our feelings. The border between individuals becomes permeable, and the social world and the private world intermix. Emotions and actions are contagious. Invisible strings of shared circuits tie our minds together, creating the fabric of an organic system that goes beyond the individual.

We have realized for hundreds of years that the actions and feelings of others can influence our own. Where we erred was in our notion of how directly we are connected. Neuroscience shows us that we connect not only through our thoughts, or because we make an effort to "conceive ourselves enduring all the same torments" that "we enter as it were into [someone else's] body"[67], but through our brains' proclivity to simply and spontaneously link the actions and emotions together, without requiring the intervention of conscious effort. The brain is hard wired to turn us into highly social and empathic animals.

7

Sensations

At eight o'clock one evening dinner is far from ready, but the first guests are arriving. After a quick round of greetings, Valeria and I get back to cooking. "Thank you! You shouldn't have," Valeria says politely. "Chris, could you put them in a vase?" she adds handing me the bouquet of tulips and grabbing a twenty-inch, razor sharp, Japanese chef's knife to cut the onions. After I ask her where the vase might be, she starts to chop the onions distractedly while her eyes scan the shelves of the living room. I look at her, and to my shock I see the blade slice into the flesh of her finger instead of the onion. I don't remember who said, "Ouch!" first, she or I. A flash of red almost immediately spreads from the wound. She presses her finger, and I press mine. I rush for some kitchen paper to wrap the wound.

Most of us have experienced scenarios like this, in which the bodily pain of other makes us feel physically unwell. Our experience of viewing pain goes beyond mere understanding, and we literally *feel* the pain, in a vivid and localized fashion, as if our own finger was cut. So far, we have seen how we share the actions and the visceral emotions with other people, but we have not yet investigated sensations. The sight of someone being touched by a feather on the sole of his foot can make us feel ticklish, and the sight of someone grasping a cactus can feel painful. What makes tactile sensations different from emotions, is that we feel them in a specific part of our body. My finger was what hurt when I saw Valeria cut hers. Somatosensations, from the Greek *soma* (the body), and Latin, *sensus* (our faculty of perception), are percepts that normally result from sensing our own body. We feel touch, when someone taps on our sholder but also pain, when we cut ourselves, sensations of cold and warm, while we touch an icecube or a radiator, of itch, when we were bit by a moskito, of our inner body, when we feel our stomach constrict, or of body position, when we wake up and know the configuration of our limbs and body without needing to look. But in the opening example, all we see is the body of another individual being subjected to a certain stimulus, and yet we feel what the other person is feeling without that person needing to give any signal. The sight of Valeria's cut, not her facial expression, made me hurt.

By now you suspect, of course, that we might share the sensations of others by activating the parts of our brains that are responsible for our own sensations. In this chapter we will see if that is true, and we will stretch the question of sharing beyond the social domain to answer such questions as why it hurts to hear the screeching sound of metal against concrete if we know that the metal is our brand new car, and the concrete, the wall of our garage. Finally we will examine an intriguing question of why we traditionally send our men to war, and not our women.

SEEING TOUCH IS LITERALLY TOUCHING

For obvious reasons, testing whether there is a mirror system for seeing people cut their fingers is impractical; finding volunteers would be difficult. Instead, together with my colleague Vittorio Gallese in Parma, and my friend Bruno in Marseille, I decided to test whether seeing someone else being touched would recruit the same brain areas as being touched on one's own body. While recording their brain activity in an MRI, we had participants watch movies of my legs being stroked by a brush, and similar movies in which the brush moved ten inches away from my legs. We then brushed the legs of the same participants with a washing glove, which we decided to use in lieu of the unpleasant bristles of the brush. The data indicated that when participants were touched in the scanner, they activated four brain areas known to be responsible for our sense of touch: one on the top of each hemisphere, and one on either side in the sylvian fissure, the horizontal fold in our brain that separates the parietal lobe from the temporal cortex. The top activations correspond to what is called the primary somatosensory cortex, or SI (S for somatosensory, and I for roman one). Touching the left leg activates the right SI, touching the right leg, the left SI. The fact that activations are on the opposite side of the brain compared to the leg is due to the fact that the nerves that go from the body to the brain cross to the opposite side on their way up. A similar crossover also occurs in the motor system as nerves cross to the opposite side of the body on their way from the brain to the muscles, which is why people with a stroke to the left side of the brain lose the control of the right half of their body.

The second area of activation, situated inside the sylvian fissure of both hemispheres, corresponds to what is called the secondary somatosensory cortex, or SII. Unlike SI, the two SII clusters responded to touching both sides of the body. Anatomical studies in the monkey suggest that SII mainly receives its information from SI, and SII thus seems to integrate information from the SI of both hemispheres. SII is a step above SI in the processing hierarchy of tactile stimulation.

So, what was the difference in the reaction between viewing the movies of the brush touching my legs and those of the brush making the same movement ten inches away? The two movies contained the same amount of movement and, accordingly, we found very little difference between reactions in the visual regions of the brain representing the sight of that movement. However, we expected brain areas that directly analyze whether touch is present or absent to respond more to the touch movies. We also hoped, of course, that the brain regions responsible for our own experience of touch would be active during this process. What we found was that the regions showing the *most* reliable difference between the two types of movie was *exactly* the SII, which had been activated when the participants were touched. Much like the team in Parma must have felt when they first observed mirror neurons, we barely dared to believe our results because people had been investigating this brain area, SII, for over thirty years, describing in great details how the area was involved in the experience of being touched on one's own body, and yet, not a single study had realized that part of this area was also activated when seeing someone else being touched. The belief that this area was somatosensory had made people blind to the visual properties of the area.

The beauty of this finding lies in the fact that, when you recognize that we perceive the actions of others in the same regions that we use to program our own actions and that we also understand the emotions of others in the emotional areas of our brain, you can conclude that, instead of being a peculiar property of individual brain regions, mirroring is a rather general principle of brain function. Although we have specialized brain areas for viewing the world, namely our visual cortex, when it comes to feeling what goes on in other people, we do not rely on a single, specific, specialized brain region. Instead, we seem to recruit those brain regions we would used to experience the same state, be it an action, an emotion, or a sensation. The exact brain area activated changes from motor areas for actions, emotional areas for emotions, and somatosensory areas for sensations, but the principle remains the same.

WHY IT HURTS TO DAMAGE YOUR CAR

If we feel our car being scratched, we sometimes wince as if we empathized with the car. If we change gears with a stick shift and hear the gearbox grind, our face contracts as if we have felt the gearbox's pain. We, however, usually empathize more with humans than with inanimate objects. Seeing a knife cut off a finger is painful to watch, but seeing the same knife cut a loaf of bread feels very different. How would the mirror system for touch react in these cases? Would our somatosensory cortex feel what objects experience?

Valeria decided to examine this question. We recorded new movies of my legs being touched and similar movies with the brush moving ten inches away from my legs. We then placed ring binders and rolls of paper towels on the examination bed where my legs had been. We filmed the exact same touching movements, but this time the brush either stroked the *objects* or moved ten inches away from them. We showed the movies to new participants while measuring their brain activity. What we found was that the sight of the objects being touched activated SII just as strongly as seeing the movie of my legs! Our shared circuit for touch thus appears to transform the sight of touch into a sensation of touch independent of what is touched.

As we saw in Chapter IV, the mirror system for actions is just as active when observing humans and as robots. For both actions and touch, shared circuits thus do not differentiate between humans, robots and objects. The mirror system simply translates what is seen into what it would feel like to perform similar actions or be touched in similar ways.

If we observe someone perform an action, the mirror activity in our premotor and parietal cortex not only resembles that of when *we* perform similar actions, it also resembles the activity in the premotor cortex of the person we observe. In that case, the observer's premotor and parietal activity truthfully mirror those of the person being observed. The same is true when we observe the tactile sensations of other human beings: the observer's somatosensory activity truthfully mirrors that of the observed human.

For the case of a human observing a monkey, or a monkey observing a human, things become a little bit more complex. Both humans and monkeys have premotor and somatosensory cortices, and the brain regions activated when a monkey sees a human grasp roughly resemble those in the observed human beings, but the precise organization of these brain regions differs, which leads to small discrepancies. As we have seen, differences also emerge when participants born without arms or hands observe the hand actions of other individuals. They activate *foot* representations that differ in certain ways from the *hand* representations used by the observed individual. When humans observe the actions of robots, the discrepancies become substantial. The premotor activity in the human observer does not resemble the electronic activity in the central processing unit of the robots, and likewise, the activity in SII does not resemble the state of the ring-binders that are being touched in our movies.

For historical reasons, we will continue to use the term mirroring or simulation to describe what shared circuits do, but what the mirror system really does is not so much mirror the neural state of whom we observe as *translate* and *reinterpret* what we see into the language of what we would have done or felt in that situation. When processing humans, this translation effectively acts as a neuronal mirror of varying truthfulness depending on the similarity between the observer and the observed individual. When dealing with fundamentally different entities like robots or rolls of paper towels, this translation acts more like a projector, projecting the observer's own experience onto the things he observes. Our shared circuits certainly don't help us realize that other organisms might be different from us. They inherently assume that we all experience the same thing, or, seen from a complementary perspective, the activity of shared circuits may be what makes us feel as if all things around us feel as we do. Shared circuits lead us intuitively to anthropomorphize or even egomorphize the world around us.

We do not quite know yet why it feels so different to see a knife enter a loaf of bread versus a human hand. The mirror systems for sensations create a neural state in the somatosensory cortex that resembles that of being touched in similar ways. Our own experience of touch, though, is not exclusively determined by activity in somatosensory cortices. Experiencing the warm and silky feel of animal fur brushing our legs will activate SII. If we look at what touched us, and see that it was our pet cat, this sensation feels pleasant. If we find out that it was a stray rat that just crawled out of the gutter, the same somatosensory activity feels very different. A similar activity in somatosensory areas can thus lead to very different feelings depending on the context of brain activity in other brain regions that tells us what is touched or being touched. Our relative lack of empathy for objects as opposed to people therefore does not appear to rely on the absence of mirroring in somatosensory areas, but on an active reappraisal of that mirroring. Prefrontal brain regions likely play a central role in this reappraisal.

Shared circuits are probably an essential part of sensing what happens to other people and objects, be they alive or not, but the result of that simulation integrates with our knowledge about the world, and is interpreted differently based upon that knowledge. Infants sometimes become surprisingly distressed if they see objects being broken, which may reflect the fact that their shared circuits are already responding to the sight of touch, but their cognitive interpretations do not yet reinterpret this shared sensation as benign.

At first it may seem odd for the brain to be so deeply anthropocentric. Attributing human states to other organisms could be grave mistake. But it's probably not. The brain has evolved to be successful in maximizing the fitness of an organism. While hunting a rabbit, a hunter will activate his shared circuits and begin to hunt the rabbit as if it had the same brain he does, even though the rabbit's brain, of course, differs in many ways from the human brain. The hunter's shared circuits will nevertheless lead him to correctly predict that the rabbit will run away from him, allowing him to strategically scare the rabbit into a trap. Getting the rabbit is what allows us to survive. Philosophical insights into the fact that a rabbit's mental life may actually feel quite different are interesting, but will not help us get dinner.

Based on these pragmatic requirements, if assuming that a rabbit has emotions that resemble yours makes you catch it faster, you should keep doing so, whether this is assumption is correct or not. Similarly, if assuming that your car feels something when it is touched prevents you from having collisions, you should keep doing so. Our own actions and sensations are the only ones we really know. Using them for mirroring all things is thus not arrogance, but the humble egocentric predicament of someone who knows no other actions or sensations but his own. Our more intellectual mind can then interpret the result of that egocentric mirroring more judiciously.

One might speculate that our sharing of sensations with objects could be linked to the importance that objects have in our lives and those of many animals. When jumping from tree to tree, primates need to understand when a branch will safely bend and when it will break. They could develop empirical rules derived from remembering which branches previously resisted their weight and which broke, but this learning would be acquired at the cost of broken ribs or lost lives. Alternatively, they could derive an intuitive sense of torsion and rupture point by extending the experience of their own body to inanimate objects such as branches. Whenever we bend our own fingers, we get a rich introspective concept of non-painful tension, painful tension, and sometimes rupture. These feelings richly map onto intuitive concepts, such as how well a branch will bend before it breaks. In more modern times, the same empathy may keep us from damaging much of the valuable equipment we use, including our precious cars. It is hard to imagine modern culture without an intuitive sense that "things" shouldn't be broken. Shared circuits that empathize with objects may have been evolutionary building blocks that facilitated this capacity.

One might even consider going a step further, investigating the relationship between our sense of property and empathy. Do we empathize and activate our somatosensory cortex more if we see our own car being scratched as compared to seeing it happen to someone else's car? The fact that neither the robot in our experiment on actions nor the objects in our study on sensations belonged to our participants suggests that some sharing occurs even in the absence of a feeling of property. A sense of property may yet further increase this sharing, and vice versa, our feeling of attachment to an object may be linked to how strongly we share sensations with this object. But we still need to test this idea.

How your pain becomes my pain

While we were studying the mirror system for touch, the German psychologist Tania Singer in London began to directly study the phenomenon that made me wince in pain when seeing Valeria cut her finger.

Tania later told me, by the pool of an *agriturismo* we had rented all together after a conference in Tuscany, that she simply posted an advertisement stating: "Couples wanted for functional magnetic imaging experiment on empathy." She invited the interested young couples who called for an initial appointment, in which she explained the study. The woman would lie in an fMRI scanner with her partner sitting next to her. Both the male and female partner had to wear little electrodes on their hands through which a current would occasionally be applied, causing mild pain. Tania attached the electrodes to their hands to give them an idea of how it would feel. The shock was painful, but not unbearable, like a pinch. During the experiment, as the woman lay in the scanner, she would watch a screen on which a little arrow would appear. If the arrow was pointing toward her hand, she would receive a shock, painful if the arrow was dark, and a non-painful if the arrow was light colored. If the arrow was pointing toward the hand of her partner, he would be subjected to either the painful or the non-painful stimulus, but there would be no other signs of his pain. Once scanning started, participants were forbidden to communicate in a verbal or non-verbal fashion with their partners, but the color of the arrows would tell the participant when her partner was in pain.

Tania and her colleagues found that, in the anterior insula and the anterior cingulate cortex, knowing that the partner was in pain caused activations that resembled those when participants experienced pain themselves[58]. Once again, it turns out that what happens to other individuals is directly mapped onto regions that deal with our own experience. Interestingly, the location of her activation in the insula fell remarkably close to where we had found activations during the experience and the observation of disgust, suggesting that the insula may indeed represent a whole variety of bodily feelings, ranging from food related disgust and pleasure to bodily pain[51, 58, 59].

Tania was the first to also give her participants the Davis scale to measure inter-individual differences in empathy (Appendix) and she found that those participants with the highest score in the Empathic Concern subscale also activated their own pain regions most strongly. The subscale contains statements such as: "I would describe myself as a pretty soft-hearted person" or "I often have tender, concerned feelings for people less fortunate than me".

Is knowing as good as seeing?

From different backgrounds and for different reasons, a number of experimenters had sought to unravel the neural basis of empathy. We all independently reached similar conclusions, that structures in the execution of actions, and the experience of touch, disgust, and pain, become activated while viewing or knowing that other individuals perform similar actions or experience similar events.

The key difference between the studies was the way in which participants perceived the emotions of other individuals. In our studies on touch and emotions, the participant could clearly see what happened to the other person. They saw legs being touched by rods or faces wincing in disgust after sampling the contents of a glass. In Tania's study, participants saw only little colored arrows pointing toward hands, indicating that the partner was experiencing pain. Whereas most of our studies in the laboratory thus simulate what happens when you directly witness what happens to other people, Tania's study and the one about disgusting stories of Mbemba from the last chapter[64], simulates situations where you *know* what another person is experiencing without being able to see the event directly, such as when you read in an email that your partner cut herself. The fact that, in all cases, the neural representation of your own experience becomes active confirms that there is more than one way to activate shared circuits. Directly witnessing what happens to the other person might be the most ancient and most natural form of input into this social system, but even just knowing what happens to another person can be enough to activate similar systems. The knowledge can be derived from arbitrary symbols or explained by verbal instructions. Our empathic sharing is remarkably flexible.

WHY BEING TOUCHED FEELS DIFFERENT FROM VIEWING TOUCH

The fact that we feel physically unwell just from seeing our partner cut her finger is a striking example of how strong empathy can be. However, we are never confused about who is actually touched or hurt. As we have seen, only a limited sector of SII is shared between the observation of touch and the experience of a similar touch. Most of SII appears to be reserved for our own sensations. In addition, SI was strongly activated in our experiment during the experience of touch, but only very weakly during the observation of touch. These differences may account for why seeing and experiencing touch feel so different from each other. Vision activates only a subset of the neurons involved in our experience.

Sarah-Jayne Blakemore was intrigued by the existence of a shared circuit for touch and I was told that she discussed the implications of a mirror system for touch at a small meeting in London. "When we see someone being touched, we intuitively understand that the other person experiences touch. It turns out that our somatosensory system then becomes activated 'as if' we were being touched ourselves," she explained. A fellow researcher looked surprised. "What do you mean, 'as if', or 'understand'? I actually feel the touch on my own skin!" Sarah-Jayne didn't quite know what to make of this statement but after the meeting, she became convinced that there was something unique in the vicarious experience of touch experienced by that woman.

To preserve her anonymity, Sarah-Jayne refers to her as 'C', but let's call her Deanna. Deanna experiences touch in a direct tactile fashion when she sees other people being touched, in particular on the face. In all of us, viewing touch activates a simulation of touch that is weaker than the true experience. It appeared as though, for Deanna, this simulation might be so strong that it feels confusingly real. Sarah-Jayne studied this possibility using fMRI. While measuring the brain activity, she touched Deanna on her body, and showed her movies of other people being touched. She then performed the same experiment on twelve volunteers who, like most of us, reported not experiencing a true tactile sensation when seeing touch. She then compared the amplitude of the activations in somatosensory areas in Deanna with those in members of the group. Deanna showed much stronger activations during the observation of touch in both SI and SII, making it so that seeing someone else being touched felt as tactile as being touched herself. The normal dissociation between reality and its simulation had disappeared. Because the activity in both her SII and SI regions were stronger than those of the control group, it is hard to know which of these two areas was critical for the difference in perception. It might even be that more extensive and stronger activity in both areas might be necessary for observed touch to feel so real.

The most important conclusion of Sarah-Jayne's example is that, if simulation is extremely strong, the normal differences between seeing what happens to others and our own experience can become blurred. For most of us, evolution has kept a brake on these mirror systems. The variations between participants in the study fell within a range indicative of them experiencing clear differences between seeing and experiencing. Interestingly, participants who, like Deanna, are confused about who is being touched when they see touch occurring to other people, turn out to be more empathic according to the Davis test than individuals who do not[68], which strengthens the idea that activating one's own representation of touch while seeing other individuals being touched may indeed be a gate to empathy. Cold-blooded murderers on the other hand might be at the opposite extreme of this continuum.

MEN RESERVE THEIR EMPATHY FOR FAIR PEOPLE, WOMEN DON'T

So far, we have shown that shared circuits become spontaneously activated while we witness what other people experience, whether we know the other person, as in Tania's study, or not, as in ours. Tania however wondered what would happen if you met someone, found out that he was a despicable person, and then saw him in pain? What if he had been unfair to you?

Still by the pool in Tuscany, she told me she had participants come alone to the scanner in a second experiment on pain. There, they met two actors they were led to believe were research participants like themselves. Before scanning, the participant and the two actors played a game called a sequential iterated prisoner's dilemma[iv], which was borrowed from experimental economics where it was used to examine cooperation. The rules are complex, but the concept is quite simple. A player can entrust money to another player, and this other player can either be fair and give some of that money back to the first player, or be unfair and keep it all. What is important for Tania's experiment is that participants become quite emotional about this game. If the other player repeatedly gives you back a lot of money, you will like him, and if he repeatedly keeps all the money that you entrust him with, you will dislike him.

Half her participants were female, half male. For half the female participants, the actors were two males, for the other half, two females. The same was true for the males. Participants thought they were coming for two unrelated experiments. In the first experiment, the participant played a series of prisoner's dilemma games with the two actors. One of the two actors, the "Good Guy," consistently gave large amounts of money back to the participant according to a predetermined script. The other actor, the "Bad Guy," behaved unfairly, sending back small amounts of money (often even zero) to the participant. After the game, participants were indeed quite emotional, and rated the Good Guy as pleasant and attractive but the Bad Guy as unpleasant and even unattractive.

After the game, Tania told her participants that it was time for a completely different experiment, this time in the fMRI scanner[69]. She positioned small electrodes on the hand of the participant, on the hand of the Good Guy and on that of the Bad Guy, much like she had done with the partners in her first experiment. The participant went into the scanner again and little arrows on the screen above the participant told him or her who of the three, the participant, the Good Guy, or the Bad Guy, would get a small painful or non-painful shock on a given trial.

Tania then used the trials in which the participants themselves were zapped to localize their so-called "pain matrix," the areas involved in experiencing pain. Within these areas, she could then measure the difference between seeing a Good or a Bad Guy in pain. In the sixteen females, the anterior cingulate and insula responded strongly during both the experience of pain and the trials in which the actors received electric shocks. In addition, there was virtually no difference between the trials where the Good and the Bad Guy received shocks. The situation was quite different for the males. Men activated their pain areas when they knew the Good Guy was being shocked. The amplitude of this empathic sharing was similar to that found in the female participants. When the males knew the Bad Guy was being shocked, on the other hand, their pain regions were not activated. Unlike women, men seemed not to care about the fate of unfair people. What's more, the males even activated a region of the brain that is involved in processing reward–they literally appeared to *enjoy* seeing the Bad Guy punished!

What makes this study especially important is that it draws our attention to two important aspects of empathy. First, it shows that activations in shared circuits may be triggered spontaneously, but that they can be modulated by how people feel about each other. Second, it shows that males and females differ in the factors that can modulate their shared circuits.

STARTING A WAR REQUIRES DOWN-REGULATING EMPATHY

Such differences in the capacity or tendency to modulate empathy may be particularly relevant in conflicts such as wars. Most countries mainly send men to war, not women. The dual strategy employed by the average man, to empathize with friends but not with foes, would serve men extremely well at war. The capacity not to share an enemy's pain renders a soldier's duty to kill the enemy more bearable, and feeling empathy for teammates will cement the army. Losses on the opponent's side would be tolerable whereas those on the soldier's own side would be painful, further increasing the wish for revenge.

The situation in women would be quite different. Pain even to the opponent evoked a shared sense of pain, not of reward. Of course, this does not mean that women soldiers would be unable to hurt opponents, but that they would probably suffer more by doing so than men. Their sharing of pain with opponents might also make it hard for them to accept the black and white image of "us versus them" that is so central to war. All these conclusions are very far from the laboratory experiment Tania performed, but more direct investigations of empathy in soldiers may provide important insights into gender differences in the psychological defense mechanisms soldiers need to set in place to perform their difficult duty.

THE SOCIAL BRAINS OF WOMEN AND MEN MAY DIFFER

Many of us have grown up in a culture in which male/female differences are not "politically correct," the central dogma being: "We are all humans, and differences should not exist." In the 1980s, the American feminist and ethicist Carol Gilligan of New York University embraced the possibility that the genders may fundamentally differ in the foundation of their ethics. She studied the way women and men make moral decisions. A classic example is the dilemma of Heinz and the Druggist. Mr. Heinz's wife is dying and the only drug that will save her life is very expensive. The druggist will not lower the price so that Mr. Heinz can buy it to save his wife's life. What should he do? More importantly, why? When dilemmas like these were given to males all around the world, they justified their decisions (be it to steal the drug or not to steal it) in abstract terms by comparing the value of saving lives to that of respecting property. Women more often argued in terms of how the decision would affect the personal and emotional connections between people. It seemed as though the two genders listened to slightly different inner voices[70]. For women, decisions were motivated by their care for other people, whereas for men the driving force was a more abstract sense of justice. This view remains controversial, because many feminists feared that Gilligan's view revives the cliché of the good, caring mother versus the just and wise father. However, Tania's finding that fairness influences shared circuits in men but not in women makes Gilligan's views seem remarkably modern and may provide a neural basis for this difference in "inner voices." Tania's experiments and those of a growing number of investigators increasingly indicate that male and female brains do, indeed, differ. The question is why.

The social reality of our ancestors is difficult to know, but modern hunter-gatherer cultures are often taken as the best guess of what life was like as we evolved. In such cultures, clear differences in role exist between the genders, and men face situations in which empathy is not as beneficial. During hunting and military activities against opposing tribes, empathy can be a hindrance, but during collaborative hunting and the social activities within their own tribe, empathy is important. For men, a dual strategy, in which empathy *can* exist but does not *have* to exist, is the best strategy. Meanwhile, in such cultures women do not usually engage in the violent activities of war and hunting, but take care of children, the sick, and the elderly and provide food for the family by collecting nuts, fruits, and vegetables. Therefore, they do not need to down-regulate their empathy as much. After millions of years of evolution under such conditions, such differences between the sexes might become deeply engraved in the genetic make-up of our brains. But, it is important to not that these differences between genders are not simply in the level of empathy, but that, despite small differences in average empathy[14], most men are just as empathic as most women. What real difference is in the situational factors that modulate empathy. We are just beginning to investigate empathy in the male and female brain and much remains to be discovered, but it's clear that variations in empathy do exist.

Such differences do not imply that men and women should focus on different jobs. In decision-making, intellectual capacities complement the empathic mechanisms we have mentioned so far. For instance, although a man may not share the pain of an unfair opponent as much as a woman, he may nevertheless decide not to inflict pain because of the intellectual conviction that hurting others is unacceptable. Likewise, a woman might share pain with an unfair opponent, but nevertheless punish him because he is a disobedient child who must be punished, or a criminal who has to be convicted.

Although neural differences cannot tell us who should do what, they can give us insights into the inner lives of the genders that can be used to improve professional training. Ignoring psychological differences between the sexes during professional education is as absurd as ignoring anatomical disparities in the fashion industry. Both men and women can look great in jeans–but cutting them with certain anatomical disparities in mind certainly makes them so much more comfortable to wear.

I CAN FEEL YOU MOVE

In 2008, while looking again at data we had collected in 2006, Valeria drew my attention on an intriguing finding. Our subjects, including Joyce, had manipulated objects in the scanner and had watched others do do the same. So far, we had focused our interest on the fact that regions of the premotor and parietal cortex involved in *programming* the subject's own actions were also active while observing those of others. What I had ignored is that the activity in the parietal cortex, while viewing the actions of others, extended forwards into the most posterior part of the primary somatosensory cortex[71]. This region is not involved in programming the subject's own actions but in *feeling* the subject's body move and touch objects. Looking systematically through all the other fMRI studies published so far, in which the same subjects performed actions and saw those of others, we found that they all report activity in both conditions in this part of the somatosensory cortex – but surprisingly, none had commented on this aspect of their results.The fact that the same somatosensory brain region was active while the subject viewed and performed hand actions suggested that while viewing the actions of others, the participant's brain not only activates motor regions as if programming similar actions, but also somatosensory regions as if feeling her body move and touch the object in the observed way. Motor and somatosensory simulation are not separate processes, but seem to go went hand in hand during action observation. It is likely, however, that the two forms of simulation may give us different but complementary insights into the actions of others. Motor simulation would be ideally suited for letting us feel the intentions of others and letting guess what they would do next, for intensions and programming the future is what our motor system is all about. Somatosensory simulation on the other hand would give us insights into what it would feel to act in that way: is that object heavy to lift? Would it strain our body or feel good to do that[72]?

SUMMARY

When mirror neurons were discovered, most people were skeptical. Neurons that respond both when individuals perform an action and observe a similar action performed by someone else did not fit into a vision of the brain in which observing of the world was performed by a set of brain areas completely distinct from those that programmed the organism's own actions. Over the years, evidence of a mirror system for action has accumulated and our vision of the brain has changed accordingly into one of a more integrated system that processes the actions of other people using the same areas that are activated while programming our own actions.

At first, this new view of the brain was restricted to the motor system, but over the last couple of years it has expanded. First, it turned out that the emotions of other individuals are processed using shared circuits and simulated by activating similar facial motor programs and visceral emotions. Second, even the tactile sensations of other individuals appear to be processed using shared circuits, both when people are simply touched and when we see them move their bodies. In the face of the evidence that a single principle can account for so many different domains of social cognition, there is no doubt that we have uncovered a truly fundamental principle of brain architecture[52, 53].

8

Learning to Share

Shared circuits appear to be ubiquitous: we activate our own actions, sensations, and emotions while witnessing the actions, sensations, and emotions of others. This begs the simple and yet central question of how mirror neurons develop. In turn, we have to ask how a single neuron can ever respond to three things that physically have very little in common: the contractions of our muscles while we perform an action, the photons hitting our eyes while we see a similar action and the sound pressure waves while we hear this action.

The plausibility of a neuroscientific account of social cognition based on shared circuits stands and falls with our capacity to give a likely explanation of how such shared circuits might emerge. In this chapter, we will dive into the microcosm of synaptic connections and provide such an account based on what is called "Hebbian learning." Though this chapter contains more details of how the brain actually works than many of the previous chapters, please bear with me. By the end of it, you will feel that shared circuits are not magical, but are actually an almost inevitable consequence of our biology.

Hebb: how the brain learns to associate

Donald Hebb (1904-1985) was a Canadian psychologist and neuroscientist. He worked for a while with the neurosurgeon Wilder Penfield in Montreal. As we have seen before, Wilder Penfield treated patients with epilepsy by removing parts of the brain that appeared to be the origin of the epileptic fit, and he hired Donald Hebb to examine the mind of the patients afterward. He wondered if particular functions were disrupted by particular removals.

Hebb noticed that when Penfield removed large amounts of brain tissue from young children, the children recovered remarkably well, developing relatively normal mental capacities. Removing similar amounts from the adult brain had disastrous effects—a finding that puzzled him deeply. He went on to study the source of this dramatic difference in the consequences of removing the same brain area at different ages and began to suspect that our intellectual capacities are not irrevocably linked to a particular brain region. Instead, what probably happens is that childhood experiences shape particular brain areas to deal with particular functions. If the brain tissue is removed before that learning takes place, the learning can occur elsewhere. If the brain tissue is removed after learning, the intellectual capacities are compromised. In a way, the brain resembles a sports team. A group of children with not particular skills sign up for the team. The coach then trains each player for a particular role: attack, defense, and so on. If a player drops out very early in the training, the team will develop without particular deficits in attack or defense. However, if the same player is removed at a much later stage, the particular function he trained for will be compromised. Over the years, Hebb realized that the key question is how experience determines the function of a brain area. To find the answer, he needed to figure out exactly what happens in the brain during learning.

At that time, a number of important features of the brain had just been identified in a rush of scientific discoveries. The Spanish neurophysiologist Santiago Ramon y Cajal had received the Nobel Prize in 1906 for establishing that the brain is not composed of a single reticulum formed by joining all neurons together but of individual, separate neurons that exchange information through synapses. In 1932, Edgar Adrian received a Nobel Prize for establishing, using the first single cell recordings, that neurons have all-or-nothing electrical activity, called an action potential, and that the frequency of these discharges represents the intensity of a stimulus. He also hypothesized that synapses could vary in efficiency, meaning that if neuron 1 is connected to neuron 2 through a certain number of synapses, activity in neuron 1 can have a strong impact on neuron 2 if the synapses are strong, but a smaller effect if the synapses are weak. In addition, the belief was that the number of synapses in the brain is far larger than the number of neurons and that, in principle, any two neurons probably have connections between them.

Adrian's vision of brain physiology set the foundation for Hebb's theory. In parallel, behaviorists including the Russian psychologist and physiologist Ivan Pavlov and the American psychologist Burrhus Skinner, had managed to transform psychology into a rigorous science by breaking down our capacity to learn into two well-studied components. The first was classical conditioning, i.e., our capacity to associate two stimuli, and the second was operant conditioning, i.e., learning to associate, through negative and positive reinforcement, certain stimuli with certain actions. A famous example of classical conditioning is Pavlov's dog, which learned to associate the bell preceding his meals with the meal itself. An example of the latter is learning to open your umbrella over your head (behavior) when it rains (stimulus) because doing so keeps the rain from making you feel wet and miserable (negative reinforcement, i.e., removing an unpleasant stimulus). In the context of such progress in physiology and psychology, the time was ripe for someone to bridge the gap between the emergent knowledge of the architecture of the brain and these laws of learning described by behaviorists.

After much brooding, Hebb came to a stunningly simple and yet powerful thought that he published in his 1949 book, *The Organization of Behavior*[73]. He proposed that brain function has to be conceived at two causally related levels: a temporary pattern of activity and a durable memory trace. An analogy to the walking patterns of sheep can help clarify this distinction. Imagine there are four grassy patches in the mountains called A, B, C, and D. A flock of sheep walks from A to B to C and back to A, but does not go to D for some reason that is not important to us. Their passage (top left in Figure 8.1) has slightly flattened the vegetation along their path and left what could be called the beginning of a trail (top right of Figure 8.1). What is interesting is that their passage is not only the cause of the trail, but the trail will now become a cause for their future passage. The next time the flock sets off it will be more likely to go along the same pathway because it's easier to walk along. This in turn will cause the path to be even more clearly visible, and they will be even more likely to walk along the same path in the future. We can thus describe their walking patterns at two levels: a temporary description of how they are walking this week (left figure) and a more durable, structural description of what trails are visible in that patch of the mountains (right figure), with a mutual causal connection between them.

Hebb proposed that the situation in the brain might be similar. When we see our very first dog, a number of visual neurons representing various features of the dog, such as the ears, nose, and tail, become active at the same time. Other neurons representing features that are not present in a dog, e.g., wheels, remain inactive (left bottom of Figure 8.1), and we are left with a temporary rule of what makes a dog. Hebb assumes that all these neurons are interconnected in a relatively random fashion at birth, but that "if neurons fire together they wire together[v]." Given that, while seeing the dog, neurons responding to the ears, nose, and tail fire together, whereas those responding to wheels do not (Figure 8.1 bottom left), the ears, nose, and tail neurons will wire together, and the formerly weak connections between these neurons will be reinforced. The wheel neurons will not become part of this reinforced connection pattern (Figure 8.1 bottom right).

After seeing a dog many times, the synaptic connections that link the neurons representing different aspects of the dog become so strong that the brain contains a durable memory trace of a dog. If we then see a nose with pointy ears peeking out from behind a wall, we think that the rest of the dog is hiding behind the wall because the activity in the nose and ear neurons now spreads through the strengthened connections to activate the tail neurons, effectively completing our mental image of the dog

The Hebbian rule "neurons that fire together wire together" is a true triumph of neuroscience because it explains complex psychological phenomena like classical conditioning and pattern completion from a mechanistic *local* perspective. The neurons representing the nose and the tail become connected without requiring any further knowledge about dogs. The simple fact that these two neurons repeatedly fire together explains the emergence of an association between nose and tail. Hebb's rule provided the first convincing physiologically inspired theory to explain the classical conditioning phenomena unraveled by behaviorist psychologists.

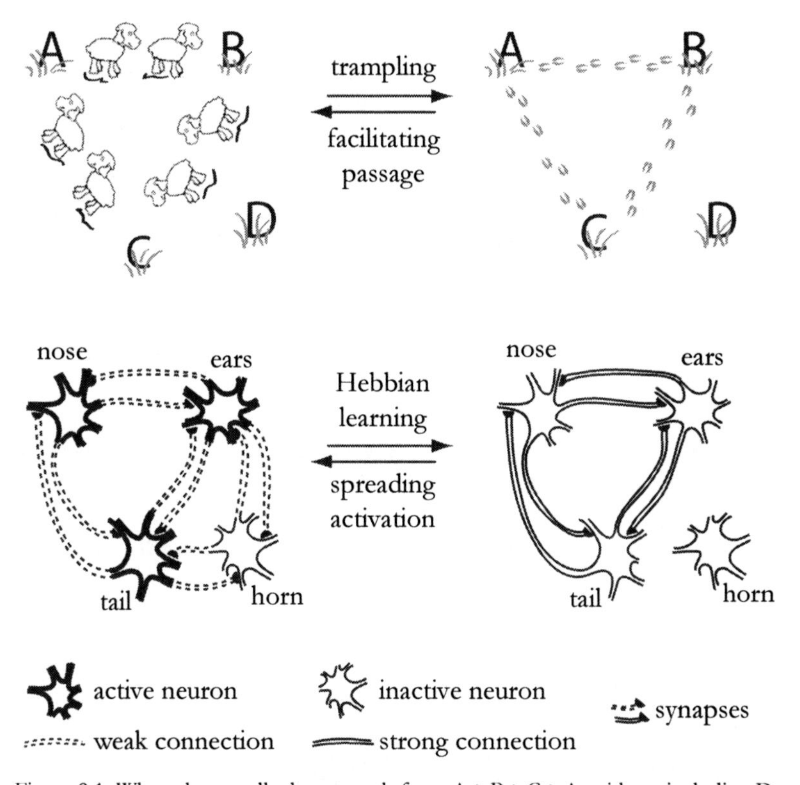

Figure 8.1: When sheep walk along a path from A->B->C->A, without including D, (top left) they create a durable trace of trampled vegetation (top right) that will en-courage them to walk along the same path in the future. Similarly, whenever we see a dog, our ear, nose and tail neurons will be active (as symbolized by the lightning in the neurons) while our horn neurons will not (bottom left). This will reinforce the connec-tions between the active neurons but not the horn neurons (bottom right), which will encouraging the recreation of a similar pattern of activity in the future.

Now, almost sixty years after his book, there is overwhelming evidence that Hebb's basic postulate is correct. Throughout the nervous system, neurons have been found that augment their synap-tic connection if the presynaptic neuron (i.e., the neuron that sends the signal through the synapse) fires at the same time or just before the postsynaptic neuron that has been activated by other neurons[74]. The molecular biologist Gunther Stent at the University of California at Berkeley has expanded Hebb's original learning rule to say that neurons not only wire together if their firing is *positively* correlated (i.e., they often fire together) but their connections are *decreased* if their firing is *negatively* correlated (i.e, if neuron A fires, neuron B is unlikely to fire and vice versa)[75]. In our dog example, wheel neurons are more likely to fire if a nose or tail are *not* present than if they are, creating a negative correlation that should lead the synapses between wheel neurons, on the one hand, and nose and tail neurons, on the other hand, to be reduced.

Hebb has shown us how beautifully the complex organization of behavior can be explained by simple laws governing the interaction between the neurons that compose our brain.

HOW ASSOCIATIONS IN THE BRAIN CREATE MIRROR NEURONS

The properties of the mirror system for action have been discussed in previous chapters and, for the macaque monkey, they boil down to at least three interconnected cortical sites: the visual temporal cortex, the posterior parietal lobe, and the premotor cortex (see diagram)[76]. Neurons in the visual cortex respond to the sight of other individuals' bodily movements; neurons in the posterior parietal lobe respond both when the monkey performs a certain action and when the monkey sees another individual perform a similar action ; and neurons in the premotor cortex are responsible for triggering the execution of goal directed actions and 10-20 percent of these neurons also respond while monkeys observe or hear similar actions[39, 40]. The visual cortex is not directly connected with the premotor cortex, but is reciprocally connected with the parietal lobe, which in turn is reciprocally connected with the premotor cortex.

The mystery of the mirror system boils down to understanding how the connections between neurons that are selective for the same actions in these three brain regions become strengthened, and how the cross-connections linking neurons with different selectivity are eliminated.

LINKING YOUR OWN ACTIONS WITH THOSE OF OTHERS

In the light of Hebbian learning, this may not be such a mystery after all[76, 77]. When an organism observes its own actions, a peculiar situation occurs in the brain. Activity in the premotor neurons that cause the action synchronizes with the activity of neurons in sensory regions that respond to the sound or sight of the action because the organism can see its own body move and hear the sound of its own actions. Within our diagram of the mirror system, this means that neurons in the visual cortex will synchronize their firing with neurons in the parietal and premotor neurons representing the same action.

Figure 8.2 shows how Hebbian learning can then lead to the selective wiring required for the mirror system to work. Let's imagine four neurons in the premotor cortex of a baby. Two of these are labeled A because they are active during the execution of action A, and two are labeled B because they are active during the execution of action B. If neurons A become active, the baby executes action A. The sound and the sight of action A now excites neurons in the temporal lobe that happen to respond more to action A than action B, and which are thus represented by the letter A in the figure. In the newborn, we could assume that the visual, parietal, and premotor cortices are weakly but randomly interconnected. The activity of temporal neuron A is thus sent to a subset of both A and B neurons in the premotor cortex[vi]. This synaptic input though finds a very different situation in premotor A and B neurons. Neurons A are currently active, and the synapse will thus become strengthened and more effective based on the Hebbian learning rule (what fires together wires together). Neurons B on the other hand are currently not active, because while the baby is performing action A it cannot also perform action B, and this synapse thus becomes weakened. After repeated self-observation during the execution of A, the synapses from the visual A premotor A neurons are now so strong that viewing or hearing the action would be sufficient to activate one of the two A neurons in the premotor cortex. That neuron becomes a mirror neuron, whereas the A neuron that did not receive input from the temporal lobe remains a pure motor neuron without mirror properties.

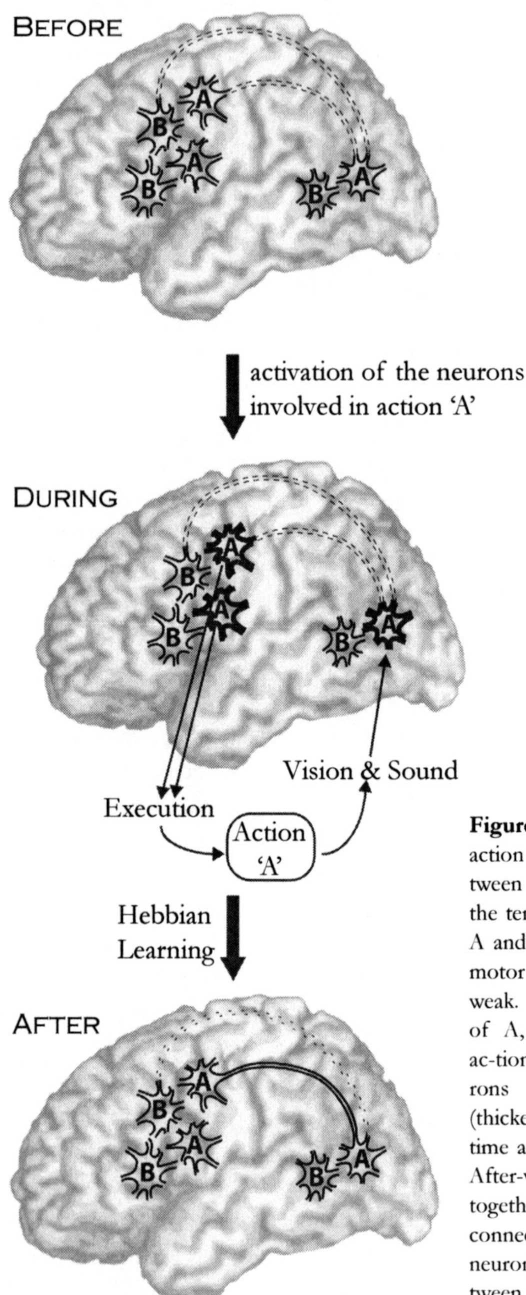

Figure 8.2: Before ever doing action A, connections between sensory A neurons in the temporal lobe and motor A and B neurons in the premotor cortex are similarly weak. During the execution of A, we observe our own ac-tions, and sensory A neurons are therefore active (thicker contours) at the same time as premotor A neurons. After-wards, since 'what fires together wires together', the connection between A and A neurons is stronger than between A and B neurons.

Hebbian learning could thus explain how we associate the sight of our own actions with the execution of these actions, but how does that help us understand the actions of others, which we usually see from a very different perspective to our own. The answer is "viewpoint invariance," which means that many neurons in the higher visual cortex, which sends its input to parietal and premotor regions, respond similarly when objects or human beings are seen from different perspectives[78]. These neurons therefore respond similarly to our own actions and those of others, causing the association learned during self-observation to generalize to the actions of other individuals. For sounds, this generalization is even simpler because the sound of you ripping a sheet of paper is extremely similar to the sound of me doing it.

The emergence of mirror neurons for hand actions can thus be seen as the simple result of Hebbian associations during self-observation. For Hebbian associations to arise, infants would need to look carefully at their own actions. Is this the case? The answer is yes. Young infants are fascinated by their own actions during the first few months of their lives, and spend most of their waking time performing hand actions over and over again while carefully observing them[79] If you ever wondered why babies do that, the answer is probably that it provides a perfect situation for Hebbian learning to occur.

The power of this perspective, in line with Hebb's original aim, is to show that there is nothing necessarily mysterious about mirror neurons. The only requirements are for the brain to have weak connections between sensory and premotor areas and for the child to observe his own actions. In principle, evolution could have had two ways to provide us with a mirror system. The genetic code we inherit from our parents could have evolved to include all the information necessary for connecting neurons in the temporal lobe with corresponding neurons in the premotor areas, and we would then be born with a perfectly functioning mirror system. Considering the vast number of actions humans can perceive and execute, an enormous number of detailed instructions would need to be stored in the genome. As an alternative, the genome could evolve coding to connect sensory areas in a rather random fashion with premotor areas using synapses that can learn according to Hebbian learning rules, and equip the child with an "instinct" to perform actions and look at them. A child's fascination with his own actions seems to be a testimony that evolution has taken the latter route. As a result, the child not only develops a mirror system, but also links the sight of its own actions to the premotor cortex in a way that can be essential for controlling his own actions by monitoring whether they look the way they should[vii]. In this view, the latter motor control function may be the main reason why evolution selected brains with mirror neurons, but once the brain has mirror neurons, it might as well use them to understand other people as well.

LEARNING THE DIFFERENCE BETWEEN SELF AND OTHER

Shared circuits allow us to relate the actions of others to our own actions. However, if I hand you a glass of wine, and you take it from me, I have to understand what action is mine and which is yours. How does our brain differentiate a visual movement I cause from one that you cause?

As mentioned before, the connections between the visual cortex and the premotor cortex are reciprocal. Although the flow of information from visual to premotor neurons can provide the visual input to mirror neurons, the backward flow of information could be essential for teasing the consequences of my own actions apart from those that are caused by external events.

Neurons in the premotor cortex that respond during the execution of action A seem to send inhibitory connections to some of the neurons in the visual cortex that respond to the same action. Given that Hebbian learning should progress at a similar rate in both directions (premotor visual and visual premotor), this parallel development would ensure a perfect attention regulation. In the beginning, when the mirror system needs intensive self-observation to select the right connections, the backward inhibition would not yet be in place, and the infant's own behavior would be most salient and attention grabbing. As the mirror system is increasingly tuned by training, the inhibition becomes increasingly effective, rendering self-observation less and less attention grabbing. When the mirror system is entirely tuned, the inhibition is at its maximum, and the child would detach his attention from his own actions. The regulation would be action specific, so that if the child acquires new actions, they will be more salient, ensuring that attention is grabbed by those actions needing most Hebbian learning.

In the adult, the suppression of our own actions has two additional consequences. First, it provides the answer to how we discriminate our own actions from those of others. The actions of others are unsuppressed consequences of external events whereas ours are those that the back-connections from the premotor cortex have suppressed. Second, it alerts us to errors in our motor system. Let's imagine we have a plastic cup in front of us and we expect the cup to be full of water, so we plan to lift it with a fair bit of force and expect to see a slow progressive lift. Our connections will cancel out the sight of our own movement by inhibiting representations of slow upwards movements. If the cup turns out to be empty, it will lift very easily. As a result we will see the cup move up very quickly, a movement different from the one suppressed, leading to a salient input that serves as the waving red flag of an error message telling us to move more slowly[viii].

YOU CAN ONLY MIRROR WHAT YOU CAN DO

If the mirror system truly develops through Hebbian learning, we would expect that very young infants should not have a mirror system for a particular action before they are able to perform the action themselves. For instance grasping starts developing only at around six months of age, and an infant at three months should thus not yet have a mirror system for grasping and not really understand what other individuals do while they grasp. But how can you find out if a six month old infant understands an action given that the infant is too young to tell you?

In Seattle, at the University of Washington, developmental psychologists Jessica Sommerville, Amanda Woodward, and Amy Needham examined that question using a simple but clever psychological method[83] They compared how well infants with and without grasping experience understand grasping–but without having to ask the child anything. Let us call the average infant from each of these two groups Alison and Anne. Little Alison is three-and-a-half-months old, which is too young to grasp toys on her own. Her brain cannot quite coordinate the sequence of movements required. Alison sits on her mother's lap, facing a puppet stage. An experimenter on the stage has a Velcro mitten, and the stage has two toys on it, a teddy bear on the left and a ball on the right. Behind the stage, a hidden observer peeks through a little hole and looks to see where Alison is watching. First, the experimenter reaches with his mitten toward the ball, which sticks to the mitten. The experimenter stays there, as if frozen, for as long as Alison looks at her, or two minutes, whatever comes first. The first time, Alison looks at the event for thirty seconds out of the two minutes. The experimenter then repeats the exact same movement over and over again. After about ten repetitions, Alison seems to be bored, glancing for only ten seconds at what happens. This reduction in viewing time is what is called habituation in scientific terms or boredom in daily life. Next, the experimenter switches the places of the two toys. She still reaches to the right sometimes, but the right now contains the teddy bear—a new goal, and other times to the left, a new trajectory for the same old object, a ball. For Alison, both new actions seem to be equally interesting. She looks for a full thirty seconds at them again, realizing that they are new stimuli that both deserve as much attention as the very first action she saw. The fact that she looked just as long at the new goal as the new trajectory shows us that, unlike for the adult mirror system, there is not yet anything special about goals for her. But of course, she has never grasped a toy herself, so we wouldn't expect her to have mirror neurons for understanding the goal that the experimenter was reaching toward.

A day later, Anne comes in. She is the same age as Alison and has never grasped either, but before seeing the experimenter grasp, she is given a chance to play with the toys. She sits on her mother's lap with a ball and a teddy bear—smaller versions of the ones she will later see on the puppet stage—on the table in front of her. Anne touches the toys a bit, but cannot really grasp them. After three minutes with the toys, the experimenter places a Velcro mitten on Anne's right hand. With the mitten on her hand, when Anne touches the teddy bear, it sticks, and she can move the bear as if she had grasped it. After a couple of seconds, the experimenter removes the toy from the mitten and places it back on the table. Anne reaches for the ball, and the ball now sticks to the mitten as well. For four minutes this little game goes on. Now that Anne has experienced what it feels like to grab an object, if our Hebbian idea is right, the sight of reaching toward an object could be associated with the action of taking the toy.

Anne is brought in front of the puppet stage, and the exact same procedure as was used with Alison is performed. The experimenter reaches for the first time toward the ball. Unlike Alison, who watched this action for thirty seconds, Anne stares for sixty seconds. Having experienced taking the object seems to have made the action much more interesting. But after ten times, like Alison, Anne looks for only ten seconds, indicating that she has become bored. The two toys are switched, so when the experimenter reaches for the ball, it is on a different side. Just as Alison had, Anne now looks for thirty seconds again, showing that the new trajectory makes the action a little bit more interesting. But now the experimenter reaches for the teddy bear—the new goal. Wow! Anne looks at the stimulus for sixty seconds again. She must find the new goal much more striking than a new trajectory. A few minutes of grasping with a mitten has made a huge difference for her brain, because she now realizes that goals are special. The experience of pairing the sight of her hand touching an object with the experience of having the object at her disposal has somehow changed her perception of the action of other individuals—just as our Hebbian theory would predict[ix].

Without the Velcro mittens, children do not experience what it feels like to apprehend an object before about six to eight months of age[84] Interestingly, children that do not undergo the sticky mitten training also only start to find the new-goal stimulus special around that age, suggesting that for all of us seeing ourselves apprehend an object is the key to understanding that there is a goal behind the action of reaching, and this understanding immediately transfers to our understanding of the actions of other people[x].

TO BABBLE IS TO BUILD A MIRROR SYSTEM FOR LANGUAGE

Hebbian learning can be applied to more than just hand actions. It could also account for the emergence of shared circuits in speech development and in our understanding of sensations and emotions. Mirror systems exist for the sound of actions, and in particular for the sound of mouth actions[8, 9, 38-41, 52] These may be of particular importance for the acquisition of spoken language because they translate heard speech sounds into the motor program for producing similar sounds. Infants have a peculiar behavior called babbling. In the first months of life, babies spontaneously gurgle and coo, thereby producing sounds that resemble vowels ("aaaah," "ooooh"). By about four months, they start to add consonants ("gaga," "dada"). From six to twelve months of age, the infants start to play around with vocal utterances, finding out what sounds they can produce. Babbling is not an attempt to communicate, but it must serve some purpose or we wouldn't do its.

From a Hebbian perspective, babbling is the equivalent of self-observation. When a child babbles, neurons in the premotor cortex responsible for producing the vocal sounds will be coactive with neurons in the sensory cortex that respond to the sound of the action. As described above, this will lead neurons coding for particular vocal sounds in sensory cortex to connect with neurons involved in producing these sounds in the premotor and parietal cortex. As a result, the infant actively trains his brain to find out what motor programs are suitable for producing a particular sound. If the child later hears an adult produce this sound, the machinery to activate corresponding motor programs and reproduce the sound is in place. In addition, the child is also equipped with the motor theory of speech perception we encountered in the chapter on language.

In adults, not only does the sound of language activate motor programs, but *seeing* someone else speak also activates neurons in the premotor cortex. Such visual responses are intriguing because babies do not typically see themselves while babbling, making it what developmental psychologists call an opaque action. How can Hebbian learning occur if the child cannot see himself articulate sounds? Infants do have a very strong preference for looking at the faces of other individuals, and they look and listen intensely to adults while they speak. The sound of the parents' vocalizations coincides in time with the sight of their mouth, lips, and throat movements, so Hebbian association would arise in sensory areas that receive both auditory and visual input. Indeed, as mentioned earlier, neurons in the temporal lobe that I referred to as the "visual cortex" actually already combine auditory and visual responses to vocalizations even in monkeys[85]. It is therefore likely that while babbling, the infant associates auditory representations with motor representations of speech sounds, and when observing the faces of other individuals, the infant would associate visual representations of certain mouth movements with what they sound like. Through this double association, the sight of someone else speaking activates audio-visual representations in the temporal lobe that would in turn trigger corresponding motor programs[xi]. In this case, not one, but two Hebbian learning activities are necessary, but the principle remains the same.

ASSOCIATING MY SENSATIONS WITH YOURS

Shared circuits for sensations are another example of how the neural basis of empathy could be laid down by Hebbian learning. Each time we see an object approach and touch our body, the sight and sensation of the touch happen at the same time, leading neurons representing the sight of touch to strengthen their connections with neurons representing the experience of touch. Such connections could be responsible for our observation that the sight of touch activates somatosensory brain areas[86], even if it is no longer the participant's own body that is seen. Participants who establish stronger Hebbian associations between the sight of touch and the experience of touch would then have stronger somatosensory activations, potentially leading to extreme cases where an observing participant would be confused about whether the touch was real or only seen, as with Deanna earlier[87].

An interesting phenomenon called the "rubber hand illusion" illustrates how little time is necessary for creating novel visual-tactile associations[88] Take a pair of gloves, put the right one on your right hand, and put the left one on the table next to your right hand. Place your left hand under the table, just under the empty glove. Most people in that situation clearly feel that their left hand is under the table, not in the empty glove. Now ask a friend for help. Have him first to tap rhythmically on the empty glove while simultaneously tapping your left hand under the table, stopping after thirty seconds. Do you now feel the strange sensation that the glove is part of your body? If your friend does the same, touching your hand and the glove at different times, out of synchrony, the effect no longer works, reflecting the fundamental premise of Hebbian learning that synchrony leads to associations.

WHY PARENTS IMITATE THE FACIAL EXPRESSIONS OF THEIR BABY

Have you ever wondered why parents tend to imitate the facial expressions of their babies? Emotional facial expressions pose a particular challenge to the Hebbian perspective of shared circuits, because we do not generally see our facial expressions while experiencing our emotions.

In the late 1970's, Meltzhoff and Moore showed that newborn babies stick out their tongue if they see adults stick out theirs[22, 89], which was seen originally as evidence that there is an inborn capacity for facial imitation, meaning that the Hebbian idea does not apply to facial expressions. More recent studies have shown that tongue protrusion appears to be the only facial movement readily imitated by neonates[90]. Accordingly the imitation of tongue protrusion is now seen as a very specific case, with a specific inborn mechanism that differs from true facial imitation. Other forms of facial imitation probably rely on different mechanisms that might very well be Hebbian learning.

Three mechanisms exist through which the infant's own emotions can be Hebbianly associated with the sight of other people's particular facial expressions.

First, the wide availability of mirrors or other reflecting surfaces allows individuals to see themselves while they grimace or express genuine emotions. Such physical mirrors provide ideal conditions for Hebbian learning because the individual receives perfectly synchronous visual feedback. In this process, neurons coding for the sight of a facial expression would become associated with both the motor programs for producing the expression and the somatosensory consequences of what it feels like to move the face in that fashion. Although physical mirrors may play a role in the development of children in modern societies, it is unlikely that they are a necessary condition for the development of shared circuits for facial expressions. Individuals raised in societies with very limited access to mirrors show normal patterns of recognition of facial expressions[91].

Second, the tendency parents have to imitate the facial expressions of their infants allows the infant to focus on the mimicked facial expression. Although this behavior sometimes makes the parents look a bit ridiculous, it serves a very important function for the infant by essentially acting as a mirror and providing the right condition for a mirror system for facial expressions to develop. While the child is experiencing genuine emotions such as happiness, sadness, nausea, or pain, the parents' facial expressions not only imitates the infant's arbitrary facial expression, but will also empathically share the infant's state, be it by smiling at the baby's happiness or looking worried or even in pain if the child is crying. In this fashion, shared circuits for facial expressions are transferred from parent to child in an intergenerational contract. A child develops a shared circuit for facial expressions because her parents imitated her facial expressions, and once the child turns into a parent herself, she now transfers this capacity to her child.

The same applies to movement of the eyes. Eyes are a social cue of enormous importance. By looking at people's eyes, we know where their attention is directed and are thereby able to infer the focus of their thoughts. And yet, we do not see our own eye movements while we perform them. This poses another challenge for Hebbian learning. Gaze following is the natural tendency to look where the person facing us is looking. If you speak to someone and that person suddenly stares to your right, you will most certainly start looking in that direction to find out what the other person is looking at. If an infant stares in a particular direction, his parents follow his gaze, so if the infant looks back at his parent, he sees that his eye movement occurred simultaneously with a change in the configuration of his parents' eyes. Such sequences of movement could help the child associate shifts of his own focus of attention with a shift in the position of the colored iris in his parents' white sclera.

One might argue though that even if parents imitate the facial expressions of their infants quite often, many instances remain in which they do not, which could result in erroneous Hebbian associations, However, there are reasons to believe this erroneous association does not happen. Infants pay more attention to stimuli with time courses that parallel that of their own behavior[92][xii], meaning they attend more to cases in which the face of the adult reacts to their own. This behaviour reduces the impact of episodes in which there is no causal relationship between the child's and the parent's facial expression. In addition, during imitation, the sight of the congruent facial expression will occur *much* more frequently than any other individual facial expressions, strongly and selectively enhancing the congruent synaptic connections. Outside of imitation, many different facial expressions will occur similarly often while an infant experiences a particular emotion, and there is thus no reason to believe that any particular facial expression will be falsely associated with the child's internal state. Certain important exceptions to the second factor exist. For example, an angry parent might handle the child more roughly, causing the angry facial expression to be linked not to the state of anger in the child but to the state of distress. These exceptions seem to confirm our hypothesis, because our reaction to angry facial expressions is often ambiguous because we have mixed feelings of reactive anger and distress.

The third factor that facilitates Hebbian learning is the presence of external factors that influence the infant and the people surrounding the infant in a similar fashion. An unpleasant smell can cause people to be disgusted at the same time, and a loud noise will make people look surprised or scared at the same time. These shared experiences cause the facial expression of the individuals around the infant to mirror the infant's emotion.

ASSOCIATING SOMATOSENSORY AND MOTOR MIRRORING

Hebbian learning can account for a variety of cases in which an individual pairs his own actions, feelings and emotions with those of others, and will also associate different internal aspects of our own actions and emotions with each other. When we perform an action, we activate our premotor programs to execute the action, we see and hear our own action, but we also feel the somatosensory consequences of our action. Our primary and secondary somatosensory cortices become active during grasping, for instance, because our joints and muscles move in our body and because our fingers feel the object between them. These somatosensory consequences are intimately linked with the motor command to execute the action and with the sight and sound of the action, predicting that while we see or hear the actions of other individuals, we not only activate our own premotor cortex but also our own somatosensory cortex, and share what it feels like to perform the action from both a motor and somatosensory point of view. In an elegant series of experiment, Valeria showed exactly that: whenever we grasp an object, we not only activate our motor cortices that make us do the action but also their primary and secondary somatosensory cortices that let us feel how our arm and hand moves, when we touch the object we are grasping for and how the object feels. Importantly, when we see someone else grasp an object, we also activate our somatosensory cortices in addition to the motor cortices as if we were grasping the object ourselves. Given that the somatosensory cortex normally makes us feel the movements of our own body and the sensations of objects touching our skin, this vicarious somatosensory activity could be critical to make us feel what others feel while doing their actions[9, 19, 72, 93].

The Hebbian linking of sensory and motor components might be particularly important for the case of facial expressions. Given that we have two motor systems, a cold one and a hot one, for controlling our facial expressions, one might wonder which of the two should become recruited when we observe the facial expressions of others. From a Hebbian perspective, the answer is that both systems become active. When making emotional facial expressions, certain somatosensory neurons representing what it feels like to have the corners of the mouth pulled upwards will wire together with neurons in the hot motor system that are associated with spontaneous smiling. When making voluntary upward movements of the corner of the mouth, premotor neurons will wire together with the same somatosensory neurons. The voluntary and emotional motor programs are now tied together through the intermediation of somatosensory neurons. All three are tied together with the sight of similar facial expressions, as described above, and the experience of similar underlying emotions. This rich web of associations is probably the reason we so intuitively feel what goes on in the people around us and also know what our own facial expression looks like even without a mirror.

THE MIRROR SYSTEM CHANGES THROUGHOUT LIFE

The true power of a Hebbian account of shared circuits is its inherent plasticity. If shared circuits relied exclusively on innate mechanisms, their scope would be restricted to sharing those aspects of other people's lives that were important over our evolutionary development. Our modern world however changes rapidly, and our understanding of what other individuals do needs to keep up with this rapid rate of change. We have already seen how infants can learn to understand grasping by experiencing grasping for four minutes, but there are many examples of such plasticity in adult life as well. If we hear a beep and see someone flip open his mobile phone, look at the screen, and look happy, we think he has received a pleasant text message. It is hard to imagine how evolution would have prepared us to empathize with the impact of mobile phones.

Piano playing is a well studied example of the plasticity within the mirror system[94]. Neuroscientist Amir Lahav and his colleagues at Harvard selected musically naïve adult participants who had never played the piano. They then trained the participants to play a particular piano piece. The participants took about half an hour to play the piece correctly on the first day of training, and training was repeated each of five consecutive days. The participants also listened to two other piano pieces composed either of the same notes in a different order or of entirely novel notes. On the fifth day, the participants were scanned while they listened to passages from the three pieces. Even though all three pieces activated auditory brain regions, only the piece they had learned to play robustly activated premotor "mirror" regions that resemble those found for the execution and the sound of actions[9, 39, 40].

This experiment impressively demonstrates how five days of practice, in which finger movements are associated with piano sounds, appears to build Hebbian associations between auditory brain regions that represent the sound of piano music and premotor regions that encode the motor programs for sequences of finger movements. Such extreme flexibility empowers our shared circuits with the capacity to adapt rapidly to the requirements of our ever changing environment.

WHY MIRROR NEURONS CANNOT BE EVERYWHERE IN THE BRAIN

For Hebbian learning to occur between two neurons, the two neurons have to repeatedly fire together and have to be initially, albeit weakly, connected. These two requirements place constraints on where in the brain mirror neurons can emerge. If I have two neurons, one representing the execution of grasping and one the sight of grasping independent of the perspective from which it is performed, these two neurons will virtually always fire together while we observe our own actions. Hebbian learning is very simple.

If on the other hand we consider two different neurons, a motor neuron in the primary motor cortex responding when a particular muscle of the shoulder is used, and a visual neuron in the primary visual cortex that responds when a vertical line appears in a particular place in the eye, these two neurons may occasionally fire together but mostly they will not. When the shoulder movement leads the arm to cross that particular location of my visual field they will fire together, but many other movements can bring my arm across that location of the visual field, and many shoulder movements will never lead to my arm crossing that location. The lack of tight coupling between the activity in these two neurons means Hebbian learning will never associate these neurons reliably.

In contrast to the stages of the visual system that happen very close to the retina, and in which the sight of someone else's actions activates different neurons depending on the angle from which we see them, in the higher visual cortex of the temporal lobe, where more elaborate input from earlier stages is received, neurons represent particular actions independent of this viewing angle. In the motor system, such a distinction also exists. Unlike in the primary motor cortex, where grasping will involve very different neurons depending on the direction of grasping and whether grasping is done with the right or left hand, in the premotor cortex and posterior parietal lobe, similar sets of neurons are involved in many different instances of grasping. It is thus a direct consequence of Hebbian learning that mirror neurons precisely emerge between the connections of the higher visual cortex in the temporal lobe, the parietal and the premotor cortex.

LEARNING TO PREDICT

In the Hebbian scenario, we neglected one important aspect: time. When your premotor cortex gives a command to your body, it takes time for the command to actually move your body, and time for this movement to be processed by your eye and visual cortex. These delays are not enormous, but they are measurable, around 0.3 seconds. The consequence of this delay is important. If you reach toward a glass to grasp it, by the time your visual system sends information about your reaching to the premotor cortex, your premotor cortex is already grasping the glass. What fires together, and therefore should wire together, with the motor program for *grasping* is then the sight of *reaching*. Of course, grasping itself takes more than 0.2 seconds, and the beginning of the vision of grasping therefore does overlap in time with the end of the motor command for grasping, but the delays in the system ensure that the vision of an action is also Hebbianly associated with the motor program of the action that normally follows it. As a result, the Hebbian associations we form in our mirror system are not a mere reflection of what enters the eye, but a prediction of what the people around us are likely to do next. And these predictions ensure that we can synchronize our behavior with that of others despite the delays in our brains.

LEARNING TO COMPLEMENT

The predictive property of Hebbian learning has a further consequence. If you hand me a $50 bill, I will happily accept it and grasp it (thank you!). Generally, giving reliably precedes taking. My motor representation of grasping is therefore active at the same time as my visual representation of you offering me an object, which predicts the emergence of neurons in the premotor cortex that are active both during the execution of grasping and during the observation of offering, which is indeed the case[24]. These neurons are no longer mirror neurons, because they associate different actions with each other, but they can be very important for social interactions and seem to originate from the same Hebbian principle.

HEBBIAN LEARNING MAKES SHARED CIRCUITS SURPRISINGLY SIMPLE

Hebb revolutionized psychology by showing that it is possible to explain the mind using mechanistic processes in the brain. Mirror neurons and shared circuits use these mechanics for social cognition.

Neurons that fire together, wire together–and wire people together, one might add. The brain has to connect visual, auditory, somatosensory, and premotor areas together because the brain has to plan actions based on what it sees, hears, and feels. Empathy is then the inevitable consequence of Hebbian plasticity in these connections.

To date, this Hebbian account of social cognition is still just a theory. Measuring synaptic changes in the brain while people develop their capacity to share actions and feelings with other individuals will be needed to directly examine its validity. However, already now we know that empathy can, in principle, be explained in simple biological terms. Empathy, shared circuits, and mirror neurons may basically be learned associations, albeit associations with truly amazing potential.

9

AUTISM AND MISUNDERSTANDINGS

We all take our social intuition for granted. We go to the movies and feel what goes on in the protagonists. We tune into the minds of the people around us as if it were the most natural capacity. But for some, such as those with autism, this capacity is reduced. Even those without such a disorder sometime draw the incorrect conclusions by using shared circuits. Given such errors, we must ask what the limits and pitfalls of shared circuits are.

THE CURIOUS INCIDENT—A LITERARY INTRODUCTION TO AUTISM

Mark Haddon's book *The Curious Incident of the Dog in the Night-Time* gives an excellent introduction to the social deficits of autism:

"My name is Christopher John Francis Boone. I know all the countries of the world and their capital cities and every prime number up to 7,057.

Eight years ago, when I first met Siobhan, she showed me this picture

:-(

and I knew that it meant 'sad,' which is what I felt when I found the dead dog.

Then she showed me this picture

:-)

and I knew that it meant 'happy', like when I'm reading about the Apollo space missions, or when I am still awake at 3 am or 4 am in the morning and I can walk up and down the street and pretend that I am the only person in the whole world.

Then she drew some other pictures

[various happy, sad, confused, surprised faces]

but I was unable to say what these meant.

I got Siobhan to draw lots of these faces and then write down next to them exactly what they meant. I kept the piece of paper in my pocket and took it out when I didn't understand what someone was saying. But it was very difficult to decide which of the diagrams was most like the face they were making because people's faces move very quickly.

When I told Siobhan that I was doing this, she got out a pencil and another piece of paper and said it probably made people feel very

[confused face]

and then she laughed. So I tore the original piece of paper up and threw it away. And Siobhan apologised. And now if I don't know what someone is saying I ask them what they mean or I walk away." (Copyright © 2003 by Mark Haddon)

The fictional character, Christopher Boone, has Asperger's Syndrome. He doesn't like to be touched or meet new people, and he cannot make small talk, but he is a math whiz with a very logical brain who loves solving puzzles that have definite answers.

Autism proper and Asperger's Syndrome are at the core of a family of developmental disorders called the 'autism spectrum disorders' that affect about one in one hundred and fifty individuals[xiii].

Despite decades of research into the biological cause of autism, we still base our diagnosis of these disorders entirely on behavioral criteria: At some point within the first three years of life, the developmental trajectory of these children diverges from that of typically developing peers. Both types of patient show restricted interests and repetitive behavior and what is most interesting to us, deficits in social interactions. Autistic individuals additionally fail to develop language at the age that typically developing children do. The co-occurrence of these seemingly distinct problems is what is called the syndrome or triad of autism.

Children with autism often additionally suffer from mental retardation. Seventy percent have an intelligence quotient (IQ) of less than seventy and are called "low-functioning." The remaining thirty percent have IQs that range from relatively normal to very high and often excel in disciplines that require analytical thinking such as mathematics, physics, and engineering. These thirty percent will tend to use intellectual strategies to overcome many of the deficits of their disorders and are called "high-functioning." High functioning autistic individuals are fascinating for the study of social cognition because they epitomize how understanding other individuals is truly a different skill from understanding the non-social world.

AUTISTIC PEOPLE HAVE RESTRICTED INTERESTS

The first domain of symptoms associated with autism is the occurrence of restricted, rigid, and repetitive behavior. The lowest functioning individuals might do little besides rock backwards and forwards, flapping their hands. Higher functioning individuals display restricted interests, for instance for space missions or math, like Christopher Boone. Others are fascinated by calendars and the days of the year. My friend, the Belgium psychologist Marc Thioux, reported the case of Donny, who is twenty-one years old and has autism proper and an IQ of about seventy. If you tell Donny that you were born on June 27, 1973, it will take him about seven hundred milliseconds to tell you that you were born on a Wednesday (it took me ten minutes to arrive at the same conclusion using Google), and he will be right 97 percent of the time[95]. People like Donny, who have a capacity that stands out from their general intellectual capacity, are called "savant" from the French word for "knowledgeable."

AUTISTIC PEOPLE NEGLECT THE SOCIAL WORLD

The second feature of people with autism is that they lack what we all take for granted: social intuition. For us, the faces of other people are fascinating from earliest infancy. For individuals with autism, the faces of others are often of relatively little interest, and they often fail to develop the feeling of connectedness that is so typical of the social world most of us experience.

How differently autistic individuals employ social cues becomes apparent in an elegant work from Ami Klin and his colleagues at the Yale Child Study Center[96]. Instead of examining social cognition in a very artificial, aseptic, laboratory situation, they decided to use a more complex and naturalistic stimulus of watching a classic Hollywood social drama, *Who's Afraid of Virginia Woolf?* For most of us, the eyes of other people are one of the most valuable social cues. We often detect a liar because his eyes give fleeting glances; a man knows a woman is in love with him because her gaze lingers on his eyes for a little longer than usual. Ami suspected that people with autism did not share this preference for eyes. What the authors found confirmed their suspicions. Typically developing individuals fixated on the eyes of the actors for almost 70 percent of the time, triangulating back and forth between the gaze and faces of the various actors. Autistic individuals spent only about 20 percent of the time looking at the eyes and looked substantially more at the mouths of the actors and various objects in the scene.

The autistic child's lack of interest in the face and eyes means that over the years of development, there will have been fewer opportunities for Hebbian learning, which could lead to a delay in the development of associations between the child's own emotions and attentional states and the facial expressions and gaze directions of other people. Given the large impact that five hours of training can have on the association between the sound of music and piano playing[94], we can only imagine how profound the impact of a lifelong, systematic difference in exposure to congruent social signals might be.

ARE SHARED CIRCUITS IMPAIRED IN AUTISM?

For a while, many thought that a "cold" parent, the so called "refrigerator mother," would lead a child to become autistic. Today, twin studies have shown that genetic factors are the primary cause of autism. Twin studies are often used because twins can develop from the same egg, and therefore have the same DNA, or from two eggs, in which case they share only half their DNA, like regular siblings. If autism is due to the environment alone, the concordance, i.e., the probability of both twins having autism if one of them has it, should be very similar for identical and fraternal twins. If the cause is genetic, identical twins should have a much higher concordance. For autism, the concordance for identical twins can be more than 90 percent but that for fraternal twins is smaller than 10 percent. Such a dramatic difference indicates that something in the DNA of autistic individuals causes their brain to develop in an unusual way which prevents them from developing the social intuition most of us take for granted.

The question that intrigues a growing number of investigators, including myself, is whether a dysfunction of mirror neurons and shared circuits may help us understand the biological cause of autism[97-103]. Two approaches have been followed to examine this possibility. First, if shared circuits are affected in autism, we would expect autistic individuals to show rather obvious abnormalities in their capacity to imitate the behavior of others, including their goal directed bodily actions and their facial expressions. Second, we would expect experiments that measure activity in shared circuits using fMRI or other methods to show decreases in activity in participants with autism compared with typical volunteers.

AUTISTIC PEOPLE IMITATE LESS

Imitation has been investigated quite extensively in children and adults with autism. The bottom line of all this research is that children with autism imitate less. If typical children see a playing partner use a novel toy in a particular way, for instance pushing a toy car back and forwards while producing 'vrooom, vrooom' sounds, they tend to spontaneously replicate the observed action. Children with autism are less likely to do so.

The same applies to facial expressions. For most of us, we have what is called a congruent facial-muscle response when we observe a person's facial expression, frowning when we see an angry facial expression and smiling when we see someone smile. Incongruent responses are the opposite. In typical children, congruent responses occur about 70 percent of the time, but for children with autism this is the case only 35 percent of the time.

The bodily actions and facial expressions of others thus influence those of individuals with autism less than they do for most of us. Given that our feeling of connection with other people is substantially influenced by how strongly they mirror our actions and emotional facial expressions, this reduced propensity will influence the social network of autistic people negatively.

Autistic children raise questions of why they engage in less overt bodily and facial imitation. Two possible answers are that they are unable to imitate or that they use their intact capacity less. Overall it seems that their capacity to imitate is relatively preserved. For facial expressions, for instance, if the children are asked directly to imitate them, both typical and autistic children consistently produce congruent facial expressions[104].

The same is true for bodily actions, as demonstrated by the British cognitive psychologist Antonia Hamilton and her colleagues. Employing a task developed by my colleage, the Dutch psychologist Harold Bekkering[103, 105], they placed children with and without autism at a table with an experimenter in front of them. The table had four disc-shaped targets on it, and the child was asked to do what the experimenter did. The experimenter first touched one of the targets in front of him. If the experimenter touched the right target with his right hand, or the left target with his left hand, both autistic and non-autistic children reached toward the corresponding target most of the time. If the experimenter then reached for the left target with his right hand or to the right target with his left hand, both autistic and non-autistic children touched the correct *target* most of the time, indicating a good understanding of the goal of the actions of the adult, but in about half the cases both groups of children used the wrong hand to do so, mainly that closest to the target. They correctly reproduce the *goal* of the action but use *means* that differ from those of the demonstrator, means that make more "sense" in terms of achieving the goal.

The preference for achieving the observed goal over imitating the way in which the goal is achieved is a property we have already found when participants born without arms activate their foot representation when observing the hand actions of other people, which suggests that they mentally simulate the goal of observed actions but use the most appropriate means for them, even if it does not correspond to the one observed[93]. The fact that autistic children are as susceptible to this prevalence of goals indicates that their brain analyzes the goal-directed actions of others in a way that is not fundamentally different from that of non-autistic children.

Although the capacity to imitate meaningful actions such as grasping a target or showing a smile remains intact, a number of experiments show that for complex *meaningless* behavior (e.g., extending your arm with your palm facing up and your thumb and pinkie flexed upwards without an obvious goal) young autistic children do show subtle impairments. However, those often disappear with age[101, 106-108].

We are accordingly faced with a dual message. People with autism are capable of imitating actions and facial expressions but do so less spontaneously, and the difficulties lessen with age.

NEUROIMAGING TO QUANTIFY MIRROR SYSTEM ACTIVITY IN AUTISM

Using a variety of methods (electro-encephalography, magneto-encephalography, and fMRI), investigators have examined whether the mirror system for actions is less responsive in autistic individuals. They found that people with autism recruit their motor system less than others if they see repetitive arbitrary actions (e.g., a hand opening and closing over and over again[99]), but if the actions are less repetitive, such as lifting a particular finger in a particular trial, the differences become smaller[100]. If they observe a goal directed action (manipulating an object), they recruit their motor system just as much as typically developing individuals. [109, 110].

Mirella Dapretto and her colleagues at UCLA looked at whether children with autism showed less activation in motor and emotional brain regions while viewing and imitating facial expressions[97, 98]. They found that during the observation of facial expressions, typical children activate their premotor and insular regions in addition to high level visual areas, in line with our findings in adults[51, 59, 61]. The autistic children, however, did not activate these regions as strongly—afinding that dovetails with the observation that autistic children also engage in less spontaneous facial mimicry. In accordance with the fact that they are capable of voluntary facial imitation, if asked to imitate facial expressions in the scanner, the autistic children in the study did activate their visual cortex, inferior parietal cortex, and premotor cortex very much like the typically developing individuals, but activated their insula and ventral anterior premotor cortex less strongly, suggesting that certain aspects of their motor simulation and emotional reaction remained less intense than that of typical children.

One of my PhD students, Jojanneke Bastiaansen, colleagues in my laboratory and I, have performed a similar experiment with autistic adults[111]. Our participants viewed movies of various facial expressions, including disgust, and later experienced unpleasant tastes to induce emotional states while in the scanner. To map the parts of their brains that are responsible for producing the expressions, we also asked them to perform facial expressions. In contrast to the findings of Dapretto and colleagues in autistic children, we found that, overall, autistic adults recruit their emotional insula and their motor regions at least as strongly as typical participants (with some of the older autistic individuals actually activating it more than typical participants), and medial prefrontal regions involved in consciously reflecting about other individuals even stronger than most of us. What was intriguing, however, is that although activity in motor regions decreased over time in the typical participants, the opposite was true for those with autism. The activity in the mirror system of the autistic individuals was abnormally low in the yongest adults we studies, of around eitheen years of age, but then increased steadily with age, being normal by age 30. This effect of age explains why Mirella found reduced activity in the mirror system in children, we we do not find the same deficit in middle aged adults. It now seems that in autism the mirror system is not broken, but simply delayed. In line with this idea, as activity in the mirror system increased with age in our group of autistic individuals, so did their social functioning: the older ones with more mirror system activity also had more friends and were more able to hold a job. This dovetails with findings from other groups that suggest that imitation problems also disappear with age in autism[101, 106-108]. Future experiments will be required to determine exactly when participants with autism show less intense activations of their shared circuits, and how these differences can disappear with age.

What excites me most in this age related normalization of mirror activity and social functioning in autism is that it shows that the high functioning autistic brain does have mechanisms that set the autistic individual onto the path of an improved social integration. By investigating the nature of the mechanisms that normalize mirror activity we may therefore pinpoint a natural process that therapies could try to accelerate to improve the lives of autistic individuals.

AUTISM IS MORE COMPLEX THAN A BROKEN MIRROR

At present, we can still only speculate about what exactly in their brains causes autistic individuals to find their social environment less engaging and less intuitively understandable, but a number of findings suggest that the autistic brain has more general challenges that go beyond the mirror system.

Elegant genetic studies have identified that certain autistic individuals have a problem with two families of proteins called neurexins and neuroligins. These molecules are cell-adhesion proteins that help to make two neurons stick together at the synapse through which they communicate, and are essential for the changes that occur during Hebbian learning by regulating how strongly two neurons can communicate through a given synapse[112]. Methods that examine how strongly different brain areas are connected with each other in the functioning brain have found that the autistic brain seems to be less strongly interconnected than a typical brain[113-115]. Less integration in the brain would have widespread consequences for many aspects of brain function, but would also affect the degree to which the actions, emotions, and sensations of other people, represented in sensory brain areas, could integrate with the individual's own actions, emotions, and sensations.

Individuals with autism not only process social stimuli differently, they also attend much less to these stimuli. They look at the eyes of other people less[96] and, unlike most of us, they also prefer artificial sounds to human language[116]. Interestingly, a brain structure called the amygdala, located in the temporal lobe, plays a key role in directing the attention of typical individuals toward social stimuli[117], and this structure seems to develop abnormally in individuals with autism.

Tying these lines of evidence together, it appears likely that autistic individuals have two core deficits. Their brain directs their attention less toward the social world and it also establishes fewer associations between processes that occur in different brain areas. Hebbian learning is disrupted, the child is consequently less socially connected, and his mirror system delayed. The process is further aggravated by parents who, frustrated by the lack of response, are less motivated to engage in imitation games with the child. As a result, they provide *fewer* learning experiences whereas *more* would actually be needed. A similar logic may apply to language development.

We have seen that inhibitory Hebbian associations in the premotor to visual direction could be responsible for rendering the child's own actions less salient, so if the Hebbian learning of these associations were to be delayed, the child's own actions would remain abnormally salient. The hand flapping and rocking movements sometimes observed in autism may reflect this phenomenon, suggesting that the autistic individuals find experiencing their own actions more rewarding because their brain fails to cancel the sensory consequences of these actions.

If you were to ask me whether the social deficits in autism are caused by problems within shared circuits, I would honestly have to tell you that I do not yet know. Evidence suggests that autism can have a variety of primary causes, including attentional and connectivity issues, which affect the brain quite generally. A salient manifestation of these causes may be a delayed development of the Hebbian associations that are necessary for the emergence of typical shared circuits. Such delayed development could account for the lag in acquiring the capacity to imitate and will in turn affect many aspects of social cognition that depend on the intuitive feeling that other individuals feel and act like you do. Such a delay could be responsible for a part of the social impairments common to the spectrum of autism, and may also impede a typical development of language. Along this line of thinking, shared circuits would certainly not be absent in autism, but would not be fully functioning. In autism, the mirror of shared actions, emotions, and sensations is thus not "broken" but merely a little bit clouded and delayed. Therapies aiming to help the autistic brain develop stronger shared circuits earlier may be very beneficial to the development of normal social functions.

HEBBIAN THERAPY COULD HELP IN AUTISM

Evidence for disrupted synaptic plasticity and connectivity in at least some autistic individuals suggests that the autistic infant may need more experiences of pairing his/her own experiences and actions with those of others to achieve the level of Hebbian learning necessary for the development of typical shared circuits. Several approaches could be followed to help autistic children develop their shared circuits.

First, imitation should be reinforced. The autistic infant and child should be provided with a social environment enriched in terms of action contingencies, for instance by encouraging the parents to imitate their child's actions more often. In addition, the child can be encouraged to imitate, which may motivate him/her to pay attention to the actions, facial expressions, and emotions of other people.

The child psychologist Brooke Ingersoll and her colleagues at Michigan State University have developed a naturalistic behavioral therapy that targets exactly these issues, albeit only for bodily actions and not facial expressions. In the first phase of the therapy, which lasts about two weeks, the therapist imitates the child's playing behavior to establish contingencies. If the child plays with a toy car, the parent or therapist will play with a copy of the car in the same way. Later, the therapist introduces opportunities for the child to imitate by demonstrating new uses of the toy the child is currently playing with. If the child imitates that behavior, the therapist praises him or her for doing so to reinforce the behavior. The therapist will also accompany the child's play by a running verbal commentary to help the child associate his actions with language. Gestures are also introduced, and their imitation by the child is reinforced[118]. All these factors combine to reinforce the child's tendency to engage his shared circuits in social situations.

Although this form of therapy is still in its infancy, it targets exactly those domains that a Hebbian theory of shared circuits would suggest targeting. In a small scale study, the therapy showed encouraging results, with the child not only engaging in more frequent spontaneous imitation but also using more language and directing his attention more often to the same objects as his parent (so called joint attention). These therapies are particularly promising if they are not restricted to the therapist's practice. Parents can also be trained to follow the techniques and can enrich the child's home experience accordingly[119], which is particularly important if one considers that the problems in autism are not restricted to imitation and shared circuits, and interventions need to target multiple domains of cognition and behavior. Therapies also need to foster intellectual capacities beyond the social domain that will be essential for the professional success of the developing autistic individual. Brooke and her colleagues are currently conducting a larger scale study involving sixty children that will provide precious information about the effectiveness of this therapeutic approach.

Beyond added interpersonal interaction, a large mirror could be placed in the child's playing environment. The parent could draw the child's attention to his own facial expression in the mirror when he experiences positive or negative emotions, with particular attention to the upper segments of the face, since the eyes are often neglected by those with autism.

Computers could be used to develop visuomotor contingencies. A computer game could show a facial expression, and if the child managed to imitate this expression within seven hundred to a thousand milliseconds, he would receive points and engaging video animations to watch. Using a webcam, the child could be asked to make certain facial expressions while shown either a live video stream of his own facial expression or a playback of a previous facial expression from the same category. He would then be asked to indicate if it was a playback or a live video feed that he had just seen. The video stream could be arranged to encourage inspection of the upper half of the facial expression in particular. The pitfall with such video game interventions is that they might help develop voluntary skills for imitation but are unlikely to improve the child's spontaneous imitation outside the context of the games. They should thus be used primarily in cases where the child has problems with voluntary imitation but not when the child masters imitation and simply does not use it spontaneously.

Finally, the most important factor, not only for autistic individuals but also for the healthy development of children in general, is true, contingent social interaction. Unfortunately, children increasingly spend many hours a day in front of television screens. Unlike a real person who will react to the actions and emotions of the child, a television screen will never do so. What preoccupies me the most is not so much that television has a negative influence on development by itself, but that each hour spent in front of the television is an hour less in front of a reacting human being. This significantly reduces the opportunities to experience that observed facial and bodily movements are congruent with the child's own states and could interfere with the normal development of shared circuits through Hebbian learning. For the autistic individual, whose brain may be less proficient in transforming such associations into enhanced synaptic connections, the loss of learning opportunities may be particularly harmful. The fact that autistic individuals may be less intrinsically fascinated by social stimuli only aggravates this situation, because they may not actively seek social encounters and might thus be even more willing to replace social interactions with noncontigent, non-social activities.

IS A BROKEN MIRROR A BROKEN HEART?

We have seen how spontaneously typical individuals recruit their shared circuits and how individuals with autism appear to do so less, seeming to find their social environment less intuitive. Dysfunctions of shared circuits are not limited solely to autism spectrum disorders. There are situations in our normal lives in which shared circuits lie to us. I remember one from my own life particularly well.

Summer, 2000. Antonella, my girlfriend at the time, and I were on our way to a friend's wedding. It was a hot summer's day in Piemonte, and we were late as usual, but we laughed together about it. I opened the window of the old Lancia Y and felt a wonderful warm breeze. The sound of cicadas was soothing. I was happy, but this happiness was not to last. Out of the blue, Antonella and I got into a serious argument. She told me she was sick of never being able to have a good fight with me. There was nothing wrong with not being in harmony all the time she said. She needed a man she could complain about sometimes. Things, she concluded, could not continue as they were.

I was taken aback. I had not seen this dispute coming at all. I thought we were having a perfectly nice day, and she seemed as cheerful as I was. Yet something had been simmering inside her for quite a while. My happiness transformed into a painful sense of distance. I was reminded of how much of what was going on inside her failed to be intuitively accessible to me. Such episodes happened increasingly often, and my sense of attunement[xiv] was slowly breaking down. Eventually, this led to the end of our relationship.

What I suspect went wrong that day, and all the other times I had this same feeling, is the fact that the shared circuits that are the backbones of my social intuition and sense of attunement used my own way of feeling and acting to read Antonella's mind. My shared circuits interpreted her reactions in the light of my own sense of happiness in the car, my love of the hot weather, and soothing associations with the cicadas' song. My mistake was to trust this intuitive feeling of shared happiness even though her smile may have just been a courtesy to me.

But the problem was much deeper than the momentary mistaken projection of my happiness. We all suffer from an egocentric bias. Shared circuits are not magic; they make us interpret other individuals in the light of our own actions, sensations, and emotions. If your inner life fundamentally differs from that of the person in front of you, shared circuits will make you feel something the other person is not feeling. In these cases, the mirror of shared circuits lies to us. When Antonella's behavior made it clear to me, as it happened that day in the car, that my intuition was so far from her state of mind, I felt blinded, crippled and hurt, deprived of the most acute social sense we have. All I had left was an abstract set of rules that I tried to use to navigate through our relationship and keep clear of crisis. It felt very much akin to what autistic individuals report experiencing in all their social contacts. I started disagreeing strongly with Antonella every now and then, not because I *felt* it was right (I personally prefer harmony to dispute), but because my conscious mind had stored a rule: "Antonella needs a fight every now and then, and it's been a long time since the last one, so put up a fight." Such conscious navigation not only drained me, but guessing what she liked never quite worked. When I had to rely on rules, I never sensed her wishes as accurately and fulfilling them always took a lot more effort. Nothing seemed to replace the accuracy of just *feeling* what the other person needs.

Now that I am with Valeria, I know how wrong I was to believe that this lack of attunement could be a normal state of affairs in a close relationship. My intuition has returned and I feel when Valeria is happy or sad and intuitively feel why. My shared circuits are now a valuable source of information again. Instead of the energy draining conscious planning I had to do with Antonella, I now feel my energies augment by the effortless sharing of joys and sorrows. The mythical image of Love as the reunion of two separated halfs of a soul becomes tangible thanks to the seamless connection of our shared circuits: she becomes a part of me, and I of her. With no one else do I feel so deeply that humans are social animals tied together by the powerful connections of shared circuits.

BIRDS OF A FEATHER FLOCK TOGETHER

A lot of empirical work has been conducted over the last decades on the factors that determine which partners we find attractive and which will provide us with fulfilling marriages. These findings have been elegantly reviewed in a book by the German psychologist and writer Bas Kast[120]. Folk psychology has two opposing views on partnership. Some claim that "opposites attract" and that we consequently seek partners who provide complementary qualities. If this were true, shared circuits would have permanent challenges in partnerships. Love truly would be blind when it comes to intuition. Others claim that "Birds of a feather flock together" and that we seek a partner who is similar to us. If that were the case, we would actively select partners with whom our shared circuits work particularly well, because the mind of our partner would work in ways similar to our own, and our simulations would usually be right.

Two lines of evidence clearly point toward the idea that similarity is beneficial to a couple. First, participants seem to find similar mates more attractive. David Buss of the University of Michigan and Michael Barnes of Yale University teamed up to ask students to describe the characteristics they look for in a partner[121]. They then administered a number of questionnaires to the participants that assessed various characteristics of the participant him- or herself. It turned out that in terms of personality, attitudes, attractiveness, and socioeconomic status, the participants looked for partners that were similar to themselves. Extroverted individuals like extroverted individuals. Religious individuals like religious partners. Many other studies have found similar things. The second line of evidence does not measure who we find attractive but examines how similarity influences marital satisfaction or divorce rate. Weisfeld and colleagues in the United Kingdom[122] examined 1053 couples and found that couples of similar education, cleverness, and attractiveness were happier, as measured by lower regret rate ("Have you ever thought of divorcing your wife/husband?" or "If you could choose, would you marry the same person again?"), how unpleasant the partner can be ("How often do you have a serious fight?" and "Is your husband (wife) really nasty to you?") and how sexually satisfying the relationship is ("Do you find sexual fulfillment in your marriage?" and "Do you wish your wife/husband was more sexually responsive to you?").

People may seek similar mates, a phenomenon called homogamy, or marrying the similar, for a number of reasons. Biologists suspect that a similar partner is likely to have similar genes. If this is the case, their offspring will have more genes in common with each parent than if the child is created with a more dissimilar parent, simply because in addition to having genes from the mother they will also get genes from the father that happen to be identical to those of the mother (the same applies to the father's point of view). Biologists also suspect that individuals seek partners that are approximately as physically attractive as themselves because if one of the members of the couple is much more attractive than the other, this partner is more likely to switch to a more attractive partner. Whatever the evolutionary basis of our tendency to seek similar partners, this tendency has a very positive effect on couples from the point of view of shared circuits. A similar partner will be correctly read and predicted using simulation, thereby creating a pleasant impression of attunement. As a result, opposites may attract, but if you look for a relationship that lasts and makes you happy, do consider the bird of a feather, and give simulation a chance!

No couple is a perfect match of course. We do not marry ourselves. A bit of surprise and some differences are pleasant challenges in every coupling. It gives us the opportunity to discover new aspects of the world and, from an evolutionary point of view, prevents in-breeding, which has obvious disadvantages. In stable satisfied couples, these differences rest on a solid foundation of similarities. The discovery of shared circuits tells us that where we are similar we can trust our intuitions whereas in domains where we differ, we have to be wary of them because they may lead us to wrongly conclude that our partner feels as we do.

THE MORE YOU EXPERIENCED THE MORE YOU UNDERSTAND

Relationships are situations in which empathy can lead to an amazingly close bond, but are also the situations where we are least tolerant of those times when we fail to understand someone else. Yet it is outside our relationships that we encounter the limits of our empathy most frequently. We might see someone swim every day, and wonder how this person can wake up at five o'clock every morning to go for a swim. The reason is that we have never enjoyed the thrill of being wide awake at eight o'clock in the morning with a rush of endorphins soothing our entire body. Without that experience, our intuition of why the other person performs this action is crippled. We might be invited for dinner and get nothing but beer to drink, and intuitively feel that the host did not particular want to see us because he failed to buy a good wine, simply because we do not share the host's passion for this rare Belgium beer he drove two hours to buy. We might go to Bulgaria and believe that they are very negative people who keep shaking their heads at every one of our proposals just because we do not share their motor program that yes is shaking the head and no is nodding. Social intuition will always lead to very correct conclusions where individuals are similar and to increasingly incorrect conclusions where individuals differ. Just as in relationships, successful social skills employ intuition in many cases, but flexibly switch to alternative ways to interpret other individuals where we have reasons to believe that they are different.

What shared circuits give us is an explanation for why certain social contacts feel close and relaxed and others distant and tense. When we successfully use our intuition we rely on shared circuits that seem to simply associate a feeling of what goes on in the mind of the other person with social cues such as facial expressions, gestures, and actions in processes that make very few demands on our explicit mental attention. When we have to rely on abstract rules ("remember that in Bulgaria yes and no seem reversed"), we must inhibit our intuition and overthrow it with cognition that requires our attention. These social relations will reflect this inner tension and feel more tense and energy demanding. Any socially competent person will use both intuition and cognition to effectively interact with other people, but there is something privileged about our intuition. I suspect that much of the feeling of the "right chemistry" we sometime have with another person reflects the degree to which our shared circuits allow us to become attuned to that person—and therefore the degree to which we are similar.

THE MIRROR SYSTEM CAN LIE: IMPLICATIONS FOR THERAPISTS

Social intuition is ambivalent in the psychotherapeutic practice as well. On the one hand, sharing the actions and sensations of a patient is important for gaining insights into the patient and will encourage the patient to open up to the therapist[49]. As we have seen in the context of couples, shared circuits can indeed provide valid insights into other people, but only so long as the therapist is similar to the patient in this particular aspect. Of course, humans share a vast amount of basic emotions, sensations, and action patterns, so many insights will be valid. By the same token, ever since Freud, psychoanalysts have been aware of the fact that we also tend to incorrectly project aspects of our self onto the people around us. A therapist who has had a divorce might project his own problem onto a patient in a similar situation. Such projections are a natural tendency of shared circuits. A therapist should always be aware of the fact that intuition is powerful but intrinsically prone to attributing our own states to others even if they may not apply to them.

LOOK IN YOUR MIRROR AND YOU WILL SEE A HUMAN

Despite the occasional misunderstanding, our intuitive understanding of other humans is relatively accurate because humans have a lot in common with each other. We share over 99 percent of our genes, have similar basic emotional facial expressions[91], and most of the people we meet will have had some basic life experiences that are similar to ours (working, getting older, breathing air, speaking a language). In comparison, we have to be particularly wary of our intuition when it comes to animals since we have much less in common with them.

Many signals do not cross the species border well. For example, when monkeys grin, lifting the corners of their lips and exposing their closed teeth, this expression is not a sign of happiness but one of anxious submission. It signals "leave me alone," "I am afraid of you," and "I would rather not fight you." Our closest facial expression is a smile. When I first started to study monkeys, this difference induced a lot of misunderstandings. I thought the monkey wanted to engage in a social contact when the monkey was actually discouraging me from doing so, and vice versa, my friendly smile must have been puzzling for the monkey.

What shared circuits tell us in the context of other animals is that our brains will associate their behavior with our own behavior. We have shown videos of a dog wagging its tail to people and seen that it leads to brain activations closely resembling those that occur when a human moves his arm. When we witness monkey facial expressions we activate our mirror system in regions that correspond to those that respond to human facial expressions[20]. Likewise, monkeys activate mirror neurons when they view human facial expressions[123]. This simulation leads to attributing our own goals and emotions to members of other species, and we inevitably anthropomorphize them. We thus have to be wary of our bias and question our intuition when it comes to animals.

10

A Unifying Theory of Social Cognition

When one of my high school teachers taught me how to describe a human experience, he told me, "Don't just describe what you can hear or see. Describe what all the senses feel." To describe what it feels like to be on the ocean for the first time, I need to describe the open view, the white caps of the waves in the wind, the sound of the gravel that rumbles as the waves throw it ashore and pull it back into the water, but also the cold feeling of the water on my feet and the brushing sensation as it swirls between my toes, the breeze whipping my hair into my face, the salty taste in my mouth, the smell of iodine in my nose, the moisture in the air. Indeed, what sets the great poets and novelists apart is their capacity to spark off all aspects of our existence, not only our vision but also our motor, somatosensory, and emotional domains.

With single cell recordings and fMRI scans, lesion studies and TMS, with all the high technology of contemporary neuroscience, we discover that the brain is in fact a great poet. The brain provides us with a superb description of the secret inner life of the humans around us. It embroiders what we see and hear with a multimodal description of what we would do, feel, and sense in their place. Like every poet, the brain does so in a subjective and personal style that distorts people's true feelings and intentions on the mirror of our own experiences but still renders the states of others intuitively vivid and sharable.

The aspects of empathy that we have talked about so far separately come together to aid in our social cognition. However, there is more to understanding others than the intuitive poetry of shared circuits alone. If we see a second-hand car salesman tell us with a broad smile and enthusiastic voice how wonderful it would be to have a rusty old Chevy, our shared circuits will make us share his enthusiasm and convince us to buy the car. At a more intellectual and conscious level, however, we know from the bitter experiences of others that second-hand car salesmen are not always to be trusted. Our conscious thoughts interact with our empathic intuitions to help us make decisions, and to help us learn from the experiences of others instead of being dependent on our own trials and errors.

IT TAKES BOTH THINKING AND INTUITION TO UNDERSTAND OTHERS

Although so far I have only talked about shared circuits and intuitive social cognition, a number of researchers have focused on the other side of social cognition, that is, how we consciously think about the mental states of others. The question that has remained virtually unexplored is how intuitions interact with thoughts[124].

Let's start with our own experiences. If I eat sushi that is not as fresh as it should be, I will first activate premotor and motor regions that allow me to eat, and later, as the food-poisoning develops, somatosensory and insular regions of my brain will sense my altered state and trigger nausea. At first, I might just continue concentrating on my work but, later, my nausea might capture my full attention, and I will start introspecting in order to understand what is wrong with me.

You might wonder what happens in the brain while we introspect, and to find out you can try a little experiment for yourself. Just sit comfortably, and try to feel your own heartbeat without placing your hand or finger on your heart or on your pulse, because in that case you would no longer be introspecting, but would simply feel an outside event just as you can feel the pulse of someone else. Just sit and listen to the inner sensations of your body. Hugo Critchley and his colleagues in London examined what happens in the brain when people introspect in this fashion[125]. He attached a pulse oximeter to people's fingers and transformed each heartbeat into a tone. In half the trials, he introduced a half second delay between the heartbeat and the tone. Participants in the scanner had to introspect and decide if the tone was in synchrony with their heartbeat or not. They found that the anterior insula and the medial prefrontal cortex between the two hemispheres of the brain were selectively recruited when participants introspect their own heartbeat. The location in the anterior insula they found was very similar to that involved both during the experience and the observation of disgust in our experiment[59], suggesting that the experience of disgust indeed involves sensing our bodily state (disgust as in "feeling sick to your stomach").

Not all people are equally good at introspecting. Certain people, called alexithymics, find it very difficult to describe and identify their own emotions. They may feel a state of restlessness but be uncertain of whether they feel anger, fear, or anxiety. People with high alexithymia tend to activate their insula and medial prefrontal cortex less than people that are more in touch with their own emotions[126].

In analogy, my experience of eating sushi is composed first of activity in the motor, premotor, somatosensory, and insular cortex. Through introspection and activity in the medial prefrontal cortex, this state can be turned into thoughts about my own state. The former creates a low-level representation of my own state whereas the latter represents a reflective thought. How well my brain can turn low-level representations into thoughts depends on how alexithymic I am.

Now what happens if we perceive the state of someone else? What if I see a friend eat sushi and turn green? Shared circuits transform the sight of his nausea and the sight of eating the sushi into activity in my insula, premotor, parietal, and somatosensory cortex just as if I had eaten the sushi and felt bad myself. I will intuitively and pre-reflectively feel a bit like him. I can additionally introspect, using the same route I had used to understand my own nausea, but this time to understand *his* nausea, based on the simulated state in myself that mirrors his, triggering activity in my insula[51, 59] and medial prefrontal cortex[127], very much as if I were thinking about my own states.

Consciously thinking about other individuals is then a two-stage process. First we mirror their states, then we introspect. We no longer think directly about other people but about their reflection on the mirror of our own states. The beauty of this view is that it does not require a dedicated circuitry to think about other people but relies on the same circuits we use to think about ourselves and can benefit from all the knowledge we have acquired about our own states and their causes. I know for instance the last time I felt bad, it was because of food, and I can use that personal knowledge to interpret my friend's nausea. Unlike the shared circuits for actions, emotions, and sensations we have talked about earlier, this social introspective stage is much more explicit, and I can give a running commentary of my thoughts about his state.

Not all mentalizing relies on the results of shared circuits. We sometimes have to think about people that differ from us. As mentioned in the previous chapter, shared circuits are misleading in these situations. Our brain then suppresses simulation and relies on a different way of thinking.

An experiment conducted by Jason Mitchell and his colleagues at Harvard supports the idea that we have two routes to understanding other individuals, one that relies on simulation and one that does not[127]. The experimenters showed their participants photographs of two fictional characters together with a brief description of each of them. One was described as having liberal sociopolitical views and participating in activities typical of many students at Northeast liberal arts colleges. The other was described as a fundamentalist Christian with conservative political and social views who participated avidly in a variety of events sponsored by religious and Republican organizations at a Midwest university.

During scanning, participants saw one of the two photos and a statement such as "I look forward to going home for Thanksgiving," "I drive a small car entirely for environmental reasons," or "I believe that cultural diversity should be an important national issue." The participant then had to decide how much the target individual would agree with the statement. In one-third of the trials, the participant had to indicate how much he would agree with that statement in relation to himself.

Some of the participants identified with the liberal target, whereas others felt themselves to be more like the conservative target. In all cases, the perceived likeness determined the pattern of brain activity. Both groups of participants activated a *ventral* part of the medial prefrontal cortex in the same way when they had to think about the similar other and themselves. This ventral region appears to understand people through the process of simulation described above. While mentalizing about the dissimilar target, they *deactivated* this ventral simulation region and relied entirely on a more dorsal region that might be involved in abstract thinking. The evidence indicates that we do indeed have two routes to social cognition. A more ventral one simulates similar individuals by relying on our own opinions, actions, sensations, and emotions, and likely gives us the richest insights into other people. However, its effectiveness depends on how attuned we are to others (empathy) and to ourselves (alexithymia). Meanwhile, the more dorsal route allows us to reason about the mental states of others without relying on what we know about ourselves. The abstract nature of this process keeps our own minds separate from those of other people and safeguards us from the pitfalls of egocentric biases. Our brains appear to switch back and forth depending on how different from us we feel the person in front of us is[xv]. Unfortunately, when we use the more dorsal route, we have to rely on a set of propositions that we store in our minds about other individuals (e.g., "second-hand car salesmen do not always tell the truth"), and those rules will never be as rich as our knowledge of ourselves.

The difference between conscious reflection and automatic intuition is best illustrated with an analogy to driving. When we first learned to drive we needed to concentrate very hard and it seemed almost impossible to pay attention to everything at once. The basic activities clogged our minds and left no room for additional thoughts. We came out of our driving lessons exhausted. This state of concentration resembles the explicit processes required for thinking about the minds of dissimilar others, and it is no wonder that living together with a partner we find hard to read intuitively is as exhausting as a first driving lesson. Once we are proficient drivers, all the basic processes have become automatic, and our minds are free to think about other issues. We can now talk while driving or anticipate potential traffic dangers. The social intuition of simulation resembles this routine because it occurs to us quite automatically and leaves the mind free to either relax or even add conscious thoughts about other people to fine tune our social actions.

During our development, the intuitive simulation route appears to function much earlier than the abstract dorsal route[129]. Even before learning to speak, infants will like a new toy if they see their mother react to it with joy and dislike it if she reacts with fear, showing that their shared circuits already enable them to be "infected" by the emotions of other individuals[130]. Only between the ages of four and six years old do children learn that other children may have beliefs and thoughts that differ from their own. A simple way to ascertain if a child understands the fact that other people have a separate mind is to use the false belief test[131]. The child is shown a series of short vignettes that feature a young boy, Maxi, and his mother. Maxi has a bar of chocolate and places it in a blue closet before going out. Now his mother comes in and moves the chocolate to a green drawer. When Maxi returns, he wants his chocolate. The child watching is asked, "Where will Maxi look first for the chocolate?" All the child needs to do is point at where Maxi will look. Children five years old and older will point to the blue closet because that is where Maxi *falsely believes* the chocolate to be. Children under the age of four tend to point to the green drawer because that is where the chocolate now really is. The difference in reactions indicates that at some point during the fifth year of life children develop the capacity to separate their own mind, which is aware of the new position of the chocolate, from Maxi's mind, which still believes that the chocolate is where he left it.

Children with autism appear to have deficits both in simulation and in their capacity to conceive of the minds of others as separate from their own. We have already encountered their problems with spontaneous imitation. In addition, at eight years of age, when typical children are very comfortable with the minds of other individuals being different, children with autism will still usually point to the wrong location in the false belief task, as if they assumed that everyone knows the same as they do, namely where the chocolate really is[103, 132]. Indeed some adults with autism still fail to understand this point, as we have seen in the case of Jerome, the physicist that thought that other people would know that a particular box of Danish cookies contained colored pencils just because he knew.

From this evidence, we can conclude that our capacity to understand what goes on in other people can flexibly employ two complementary routes. One relies on simulation and can provide an intuitive gut feeling of what goes on in others can flow into a more explicit verbal line of thought that contemplates the reflection of the others' states in the mirror of our shared circuits. In that route, the world of intuition can go hand in hand with the world of thought, and it is this powerful combination that is so important in romantic relationships[133]. The other more abstract route is capable of dealing with differences between us but is less rich and develops later in life. The two routes dovetail, one suppressing the other depending on how similar we believe the person in front of us to be. These two facets of social cognition combine to unleash the true power of our social competence.

I LEARN WHAT YOU LEARN

Learning from others is the safest and most effective way to gain knowledge, and modern humans excel at this skill. Whereas most animals are limited to very specific habitats, humans have colonized the world, learning to live in the most hostile environments. The discovery of mirror neurons for actions has played a very important role in understanding the neural basis of this skill. If one of us were thrown alone into the Arctic, chances are that we would die. An Inuit born in the same place will thrive because she can learn from the members of her group how to survive. If she sees her father spear a seal, her mirror system will activate motor programs for cutting a hole in the ice, standing still, waiting, and throwing the spear at the seal. Her brain's activation of that sequence of movements will one day enable her to hunt her own seal. Mirror neurons empower her with the faculty to transform an observed goal (e.g., spearing the seal) into a motor program that achieves a similar result.

An explanation based on mirror neurons alone has a problem however. We see people perform actions all the time, some successfully, some less successfully. Mirror neurons per se would make us share equally the successful and the unsuccessful actions of others. Clearly this is not the best approach toward social learning. If we see someone do something and obtain a desirable outcome, we should learn that behavior, but if the outcome is of no interest, we should not. If it leads to a very undesirable outcome, we should remember the action, but in order to make sure we do *not* to do it.

The psychologist Burrhus Frederic Skinner at Harvard has contributed greatly to our understanding of the plasticity of behavior by showing how, for all higher animals, ranging from insects to humans, the frequency of any behavior will increase if this behavior leads to reward and its frequency will decrease if it leads to punishment. Per se, this learning mechanism applies to learning what is profitable or damaging for the organism itself. For instance, we have to learn as children that touching a hot plate is unpleasant, but as adults the sheer thought of touching one is painful and the action unlikely.

In the brain, such learning occurs because reward and punishment regulate the release of acetylcholine and dopamine. These neurotransmitters tell the brain "Hey, you better remember this" and do so in part by enhancing Hebbian plasticity. As a result, we remember very pleasant and very unpleasant episodes of our lives so much better than the ones that had no particular consequences. Those events that lead to unexpected reward lead to the release of dopamine and acetylcholine, which will increase the frequency of that behavior by causing synaptic changes that strengthen the associations between the situation and the behavior. If we go to a restaurant without much expectation and get really good food, our brain will release dopamine and acetylcholine and we will go there more often. Once we expect very good food there, and get very good food, our dopamine system will no longer release dopamine. This does not mean that we will no longer go there, but simply that we will not further increase our frequency of doing so. If we get disappointing food, the dopamine level will go down, the acetylcholine level up, and the situation will be remembered well, but the association between the situation and the behavior will be reduced, and so the frequency of our visits will decline.

Through dopamine and acetylcholine, the brain of most animals is equipped with a mechanism that allows them to learn based on the outcome of their own actions. If an animal behaves in a particular way in a particular situation, three aspects, known as the triangle of learning, are relevant: the situation, the behavior, and the outcome.

The discovery of shared circuits for both actions and emotions places a new perspective on the problem of social learning. Imagine a group of early humans entering a new patch of forest with strange fruits all over the trees. None of the food you know is in reach, and your stomach is growling. You could try all the fruits yourself, but you would run a serious risk of getting poisoned and dying. A much better way is to observe what other people do. If you see a local individual bite into a red fruit and look very happy, three things will happen in your brain. First, you will activate premotor, parietal, and somatosensory programs for picking and eating these fruits because your mirror system makes you share his actions. Second, you will activate visual representations of the situation: the forest and this particular fruit. Third, you will activate regions of the brain that share the positive outcome of the behavior[51, 59]. Within the mirror of shared circuits you now vicariously share the whole triangle of individual learning: your (simulated) action, your (simulated) satisfaction, and the situation and particular fruit. You then need no particular mechanism for social learning, but your archaic mechanism for individual learning is now vicariously fed all the information needed to learn. As a result, you will associate eating that fruit with this particular situation and learn to eat the fruit.

If, on the other hand, you see your friend eat a red pod, become red in the face, spit it out and make an expression of fear and pain, your shared circuits will create a different learning triangle. The action of eating and the situation of forest and red pod will be associated with the negative outcome of pain. As a result, the event will be remembered, but the negative vicarious outcome will lead to dopamine levels going down and the association between pods and eating being weakened. Whereas the mirror system for action thus responds in similar ways while eating the fruit and the pod, the shared circuits for pain and pleasure will change the learning consequence dramatically. The combination of two shared circuits, that for actions and that for emotions, thus turns a core system of individual learning that we share with all other animals into a powerful system for vicarious social learning.

Given that reading about emotional situations or about actions activates a similar set of circuits to viewing the same situations, reading the story of someone eating pods and feeling the burning pain of hot chili peppers can be a strong vicarious learning experience as well[26, 134]. In light of the discoveries of shared circuits, vicarious learning becomes trial and error learning, with the trial and the error being mirrored on the observer's own motor programs and reward mechanism.

IMPLICATIONS FOR TEACHING: PUNISHMENT AND REWARD IN PUBLIC

Teachers have perfected pedagogical methods over thousands of years. Their experiences have lead to the development of teaching methods that have foreshadowed much of the advice that can be derived from the discovery of shared circuits.

A common practice of teaching is group teaching. A group of twenty students sit together and see the teacher demonstrate a particular skill, the Fosbury flop for instance. The teacher then asks the first pupil to jump, and will praise the child in front of all his classmates for a successful jump. By doing so, all the fellow pupils will have seen the skill again, and vicariously shared the success of that student. If, in the meantime, one of the students has done something forbidden, such as climbing up the wall at the back of the gym, the teacher will not take him to the privacy of his office, but instead scold him publicly for all other students to see. The public punishment will not only change the pupil's behavior but vicariously warn the other students not to act in that way. Both these practices are exactly what the discovery of shared circuits would encourage. Witnessing the combination of what other people do and the success and failures this triggers is a valuable personal learning experience.

Shared circuits give us very clear and important advice in the case of security measures. In many working environments, security measures are there to protect us from rare incidents. In construction sites, wearing a hard-top hat is a nuisance because they are hot and cumbersome. Given that the likelihood of something falling on your head is small, many workers fail to wear them. Showing a graphic movie of an accident, in which a heavy object falls on a worker resulting in him being in a wheelchair with his family losing the main source of income, will be a very unpleasant vicarious experience, but one that will strongly activate shared circuits. The construction workers will be much more likely to wear their helmets in the future.

As we have seen for the case of pain, the relationship between people will influence the degree to which they share each other's emotions[69]. For men in particular, seeing pain can turn into pleasure if the other person was unfair. In the classroom this means that, for vicarious reward and punishment to work, it is essential that pupils have positive feelings toward each other. If this is not the case, seeing a fellow student being punished may fail to create the right learning triangle, because the reward of seeing him punished may now result in an increase in the association between the behavior and the situation. Conversely, seeing a student being praised for good homework can trigger very negative feelings in the peers if they see each other in competition. Measures to increase the "team feeling" within the classroom would likely directly improve the degree of vicarious learning among pupils—besides making school a more pleasant experience for everyone involved.

In traditional learning environments, most teachers are very aware of these issues, and shared circuits can only help them understand why these methods work. In distance learning the situation may be different. Internet learning programs may not necessarily share the learning experiences of one student with the other students. In these fields, the discovery of shared circuits should be taken as a powerful reminder that graphically witnessing the learning experiences of other students can indeed be a valuable part of the learning experience.

11

Empathic Ethics and Psychopathy

Imagine you are driving back from work and see a man by the side of the road with blood all over his hand, which is pressed against his wounded leg. He is wincing in pain. He calls desperately to you for help. There is nobody else around. You think about the mess his blood will create in your car, and the two hundred dollars it will cost to have your seats cleaned. Would you leave him by the side of the road to save your leather upholstery? Of course not. How would you rate a man that would decide not to help in this situation, with 0 being a moral monster, 5 your average Joe, and 10 Mother Teresa?

Alternatively, imagine, you get home to find a letter from a reputable NGO asking for two hundred dollars to provide food and medical care to save starving people in Africa. You have just heard on NPR that this NGO is impeccably trustworthy. Would you donate the two hundred dollars? Some might, but most people probably won't. Now, on the same ten-point scale, how would you rate a person that decides not to donate the two hundred dollars?

Most people around the world rate the former man wickeder than the latter. But if you think about it, why should they? In the first case, we feel that helping a guy in need is more important than the two hundred dollars it would cost to clean our leather seats. Of course, there is nothing odd about that. And the second case? Aren't we also talking about two hundred dollars against saving a life? The only real difference is that in the former situation, the person in need is directly in front of us, and in the second example the people in need are far away.

You might object: "You never know with those NGOs—where

will the money go?" But the story just specified that NPR reported this particular organization as highly reliable. "Well, it's not the same. If I don't help the guy on the side of the road, he might lose his leg, whereas the people in Africa will get helped by someone else". Really? The likelihood of someone else helping the guy on the street is as small as that of other people donating enough money to the people of Africa for your money not to make a life-or-death difference for one of them.

If you keep pressing the issue like this, at some point most people will stop arguing and say something like: "I don't know why, it just *feels* different." Or you might agree with me on an intellectual level, but next time Oxfam sends you a letter, you will still trash it and feel relatively okay about it. Why do we feel so differently about these two stories?

For a long time, ethics was the domain of philosophers. From the antique Greek philosophers to Kant, most agreed that moral decisions should and must be the act of conscious reflection. Ethics is the objective weighing of pros and cons, good and bad, utility and harm on the balance of justice. To be ethical, you have to think clearly and dispassionately. Emotions only fog this process.

If you buy this rationalist point of view, given that humans may be the only species endowed with cool logical thinking, we might have the monopoly on ethics. Animals cannot have a sense of good or bad because they cannot think. We all have a weak spot for believing that we are one-of-a-kind. Considering how hard it can sometimes be to do the right thing, believing that doing so elevates us to unique moral heights helps. Psychology and neuroscience now tell us a different story. Shared circuits might be much more powerful than intellect when it comes to morals. We do not primarily think about whether it is right or wrong to make people suffer. We feel it.

ETHICS HAS MORE TO DO WITH FEELINGS THAN WITH THINKING

Psychologists such as Joshua Greene of Harvard or Jonathan Haidt of the University of Virginia have come to the conclusion that conscious thinking is not the source of our moral decisions. We do not help the first guy and refrain from donating the money to the people of Africa because we thought about it and came to the conclusion that this is the best possible decision. Instead we simply *feel* compelled to do so. If someone then asks us why, we start to invent reasons we can communicate with words.

Take the story of Julie and Mark, a brother and sister who, staying alone in a cabin one night, decide that it would be interesting and fun if they tried making love. Julie was already taking birth control pills, but Mark uses a condom too, just to be safe. They both enjoy making love, but they decide not to do it again. They keep that night as a special secret, which makes them feel even closer to each other. What do you think about that? Was it okay for them to make love?

Most people who hear the story immediately say it was wrong for the siblings to sleep together. If asked why however, they seem to have a tough time answering. Reasons such as, "well, if siblings have kids, they might be malformed," come up, but with both using birth control, what are the odds? People argue that the siblings might be emotionally hurt by the experience, but the story explicitly states they were not. Sooner or later, people resign again and declare: "I don't know, I can't explain it, I just know it's wrong."[135].

Moral sentiment of right or wrong does not seem to originate from or depend on reason, or else disproving the reasons should radically change the way we feel about the problem, which is not the case. Arguing with people's intellectual reasoning very seldom changes their decisions. Somehow we just "feel" that something is right or wrong. Of course, our moral decisions are not entirely impermeable to reasoning. For example imagine your friend Dave tells you that he is cheating on his girlfriend Beatrice. Beatrice however is also a good friend of yours. Now Beatrice asks if you think that Dave is cheating on her—an uncomfortable predicament. You either betray Dave's trust, or you lie to Beatrice. If you have time, you'll probably grab a phone and ask other friends for advice. Your friend might show you new sides to the story, and these new sides may evoke new and different gut feelings. Before, your gut feeling may have been driven by what it would feel like to find out that your boyfriend cheats on you, but then our friend on the phone may ask: "Well, if you were Beatrice, wouldn't you prefer to know?" And this may change your feelings. What is clear, though, is that our *feelings* will be the primary motive of our behavior, and only if talking it over with friends changes our *feelings* will we dramatically change our decision. This finding carries the simple advice that if you want to change people's ideas on whether a moral issue such as abortion is good or bad, coming up with a list of scientific reasons will do you little good. You have to make them see the problem from a perspective that is linked with other emotions to make them *feel* differently about it.

So, ethics is not so much moral *reasoning*, but more of a moral *feeling*. Gut feelings are the acting judges in the court of morals. This, however, leaves the question of *why* we have moral feelings unanswered. If animals, including humans, are the result of the "survival of the fittest," as the nineteenth century British economist Herbert Spencer put it, why should they ever have bad *feelings* about the bleeding man on the side of the street?

SHARED CIRCUITS ARE OUR MORAL VOICE

As we have seen in the previous chapters, shared circuits for actions, emotions, and sensations combine to make us share the actions, emotions, and sensations of others. If we now go back to the example of the man on the side of the street, without shared circuits, what we would be left with is a simple decision. If we help him, we will have blood all over our seats. We know about Hepatitis C, HIV, and so on, and the idea of our kids playing on these seats later on makes us feel almost nauseous. What would we get in return? Maybe a thank you, but more likely, long questionnaires in the hospital or maybe even the risk that he dies in the car and that we could be suspected of murder. If we do not help him on the other hand, nobody need ever know, and we could be home in time for dinner! Quite a simple decision really.

With shared circuits, the equation becomes a little more complex. If we help him, the sight of his relieved face and the thankful tone of his voice will make us share the warm feeling of trust in humanity that being helped evokes. If we don't help him, the pain we feel at the sight and memory of his bleeding leg will continue to make us suffer. With shared circuits our choice might swing the other way.

Shared circuits make you take other people's predicament into account, but this doesn't necessarily mean they are really a key factor in moral decisions. However, a number of neuroimaging studies indicate that they are. As we saw earlier, seeing other people's emotions, be it disgust, happiness, or pain, activates the same regions of the insula that are active while we experience similar emotions, and the same regions also become active if we read about other people's predicaments[26]. What we don't know is whether this area is also important for our moral decisions,

Joshua Green and his colleagues examined this question by measuring brain activity while people made difficult moral decisions[136]. They gave people the following kind of scenarios: "Enemy soldiers have taken over your village and they have orders to kill all remaining civilians. You and some of other townspeople have sought refuge in the cellar of a large house. Outside you hear the voices of soldiers who have come to search the house for valuables. Your baby begins to cry loudly, so you cover his mouth to block the sound. If you remove your hand from his mouth his crying will summon the attention of the soldiers who will kill you, your child, and the others hiding out in the cellar. To save yourself and the others you must smother your child to death. Is it appropriate for you to smother your child in order to save yourself and the other townspeople?" The researchers found that it takes people a long time to decide what to do in these situations, and the exact same location of the insula we find to be important for sharing other people's emotions, was involved in making these decisions.

At this point, you may say that shared circuits may make us share the pain of others but that our decisions to help or not to help may depend on something entirely different. After all, if the only reason we helped other people were the fact that this would stop the vicarious pain we feel while we view them suffer, helping would be nothing more than a subtle form of egoism. We wouldn't really help others because of a selfless and moral feeling of generosity but simply to egoistically stop the vicarious pain other people's pain create inside of us.

A study by social psychologist Daniel Batson and colleagues at the University of Kansas shows that our moral sentiments are indeed partially driven by the aversion of sharing other people's pain. They had subjects watch another subject get painful electroshocks, supposedly within a learning experiment. Half of the people knew they would need to watch the entire session of twelve electro-shocks. The other half knew that the other subject would get twelve shocks, but that they only needed to watch two of them.

After the first two shocks, the observers were asked whether they would be willing to help the other person by taking her place, and if so, how many shocks they would be willing to take. If the reason people offered to help was in part egoistical, in order to reduce visually triggered vicarious pain, people that needed to watch all ten remaining trials would expect to experience more vicarious pain and should therefore help more. If helping behavior were dictated by less selfish motivations, the knowledge that the other person will get another ten shocks should lead to equal helping behavior in both cases. Results were mixed. People that could leave right away still decided to take on about a third of the other persons electroshocks, showing that helping can be triggered by sympathy without a prospect of future vicarious pain, but those that had to stay chose to take up to 60 percent more electroshocks, showing us that the more pain people expect to have to vicariously share, the more they will help.

Not all people are equally empathic. Scales such as Davis's empathy questionnaire measure such differences[14]. The fact that people that rank higher on personal distress in this questionnaire activate their own emotions more strongly while witnessing those of others predicts that they would help other people more. This is indeed the case, but the relationship changes with age. Young infants already share the distress of others: entire rooms of newborns start screaming if one of them screams, as if they all shared his distress. Helping behavior however only starts later on, once someone understands that the shared sentiment is not his own pain, but that of someone else and that helping that other person is a way to reduce one's own pain. In empathy scales, this is reflected by a transition from more personal distress, i.e., feeling uncomfortable while viewing the pain of others, to a more mature empathic concern, i.e., feeling an urge to help in the face of other people's pain.

ANIMAL COMPASSION

If shared circuits are at the basis of our ethics and care of others, the fact that animals have mirror neurons would suggest that they might at least have some form of ethics. Is this indeed the case? The answer is yes.

Imagine you are sitting in a prison cell and are hungry. Two chains dangle from the ceiling, and if you pull either one of the chains, a little piece of bread comes out of a delivery system. Given that you are hungry, you will pull the chain over and over again to get food. But then something changes. Each time you pull one of the chains, someone in the next cell starts to scream. Would you stop using that chain? Most of us would. We are humane and take pride in that. The psychiatrist and psychoanalyst Jules Masserman and his coworkers at Northwestern University Medical School found that monkeys do the same[137]. Virtually all of them preferred going hungry to pulling a chain that would give them food and cause another monkey to suffer. Some of the monkeys stopped pulling the chain entirely for twelve days after witnessing just once that it causes another monkey distress. Given that in the experiment, the wall separating the two monkeys was transparent, the electro-shocked monkey could see who pulled the chain. Did the other monkey just stop pulling the chain because he was scared of retaliation? No. Macaques live in a very hierarchical world, in which smaller monkeys don't hit bigger monkeys. However whether the electroshocked monkey was smaller or bigger than the monkey with the chains to pull made no difference. What *did* matter was how well the monkeys knew each other. If they shared a home cage, monkeys were even more reticent to inflict pain on each other, even if the electro-shocked monkey was too small to retaliate. Just like humans, monkeys seem to feel bad about hurting others–particularly if they know each other.

Let us not misunderstand this finding. In the years I have worked with macaques, I have seen them hurt each other badly, even bite off entire fingers in fights. They are aggressive animals, prepared to use extreme violence to climb up the social ladder. What the study shows, however, is that genuine empathic feelings and moral sentiments exist in these monkeys–even if they can coexist with brutal aggression–just as humans can be empathic with their children in the evening, after a day of work as a warden in a concentration camp.

Not pulling a chain if you have another chain to choose from is one thing, but humans, you might argue, risk their lives for others! Surely, no animal would ever do that. The English primatologist, Jane Goodall, lived with chimpanzees in Tanzania for almost forty-five years, and her testimony, collected in her book *Through a Window*, shows us that chimpanzees can be just as heroic as humans. "In chimpanzee society, although most risk-taking is on behalf of family members, there are examples of individuals risking injury if not their lives to help non-related companions. [The chimp named] Evered once risked the fury of adult male baboons to rescue adolescent Mustrad, pinned down and screaming, during a baboon hunt . . . Chimpanzees cannot swim and, unless they are rescued, will drown if they fall into deep water . . . One adult male lost his life as he tried to rescue a small infant whose incompetent mother had allowed it to fall into the water" (p. 213).

Moral Feelings and Learning

During development, something powerful happens to our moral sentiments. As young children, we may steal toys from our friends. If we then see our friend crying and our parents being angry, we regret our actions but at that point the harm is already done. As adults, the sheer prospect of betraying our partner is enough to make us feel guilt. What happened? Psychologist talk of the internalization of values to refer to the fact that if our parents felt angry about certain behaviors of ours, we "internalize" their values and start to have negative feelings about the behavior ourselves. Shared circuits in a learning brain help us understand how we internalize moral values.

As we have seen in the context of learning by observation, all higher organisms use a learning mechanism called "operant conditioning," in which the outcome of an action determines whether we repeat or avoid that action in the future. This powerful individual learning mechanism *per se* has nothing social about it. In combination with shared circuits, however, it becomes a tool for socialization. If we steal our friend's toys, making our friend cry and our parents angry, we will share their sorrow and anger, and those emotions will become associated with the behavior of stealing. As a result, we will start to feel bad about stealing and will steal less. If on the other hand we comfort a weeping friend, we will share his gratitude and feel increasingly positive about that type of action. A decision to steal or not to steal becomes dominated by the feelings we have learned to associate with these actions–feelings that now precede the action, and can therefore prevent it—instead of having to wait and discover what our actions will do to others. This is why pointing out to our children how they make other people feel can help accelerate moral socialization.

THE EVOLUTIONARY RIDDLE: WHY DO SELFISH GENES CARE ABOUT OTHERS?

Shared circuits help us understand the nature of our moral feelings. Through them, helping others means helping yourself and feels good because it creates a history of shared joy, whereas harming others means harming yourself and feels bad because it creates a history of shared pain. Biologists call this the *proximal* cause of moral sentiments, i.e., what causes them in the here-and-now. An entirely different question is how we came to have moral feelings over the eons of evolution, which is what biologists call their *ultimate* cause. Scientists wondered why animals evolved to care about others, because it seems like a waste of energy in a world dominated by the survival of the fittest.

Parents care for their children. For animals, that means giving up a lot of food and risking their lives. For humans it means sleepless nights and college funds. Explaining such generosity is simple. If a gene promotes parental care, the children will inherit the same gene in 50 percent of the cases (because half the genes come from the other parent). By making sure that these children are well cared for, the gene therefore promotes itself—through its copies in the children. One way to be successful in Darwinian selection is therefore to care about your children. But this doesn't explain why we want to help the guy by the side at the road in the opening example.

For a long time, evolutionary biologists did not understand why any animal would ever help someone in a situation like that. Then the concept of *mutualism* became popular. For solitary animals like cats, helping other cats is of little use if they are not related. For a monkey, who lives in a social group, things are different. Monkeys in the wild do very poorly if they are separated from their group. Social groups are where morality and empathy become a strategy for survival. Imagine two different groups of monkeys. One group has a gene that makes the monkeys share the other monkeys' pains and joys (i.e., they have shared circuits); the other group does not. Now imagine a predator coming into the two groups. In the first, the predator may get hold of one of the monkeys, but his distress calls will motivate the others to help. Together they can fight the predator away, and everyone survives. The concept of mutualism is important here because those that help today just have costs today, because the predator might hurt them while they help, but tomorrow they might be the victim and receive the benefit of someone else's help. A given monkey's benefit in helping is indirect, through the potential of being helped back.

Over many episodes, the benefits of being helped can then outweigh the cost of helping. Though everyone might get little scratches and bruises, they will all survive. In the other group, the same predator will isolate one of the monkeys, and the others will just run away. Although good news for the runaways in the short run, because as long as the predator is feeding on a monkey, he will not attack another, in the long run, it might sometime be their turn, and nobody will be there to defend them.

On closer inspection, the reasoning seems flawed. The group as a whole would benefit from such altruistic genes—but groups do not have genes, individuals do. If a single monkey develops an empathic gene in the second, selfish group, that monkey would come to the rescue of others and risk his life, without ever getting help back. So how can altruism get started?

The first important factor is that most modern primates are matrilocal, which means that males are kicked out and go to neighboring groups but females stay. As a result most, if not all, of the females in a group are direct blood relatives of each other. For males the situation is a bit different, because though the dominant males may be fathers to many of the children, the novel male arrivals will not be. Overall, males are less related to the other members of the group than the females.

A certain difference in altruism seems inevitable. When a female monkey rescues another within her group, there is a fairly high chance that that monkey will have a copy of the same altruistic gene, and the rescuing monkey is therefore promoting her own genes. The chance that the group member has the gene is lower than if she helps her own children, however, and so she will do less for group members than for her own children, but more for group members than for members of neighboring groups.

I think that we all experience a similar gradient in our own generosity. We will do close to everything for our children and direct relatives, less for the guy by the side of our neighborhood road, and even less for the distant people of other continents. Distance matters. Our reticence to donate to anonymous children in Africa might have something to do with those simple laws of kinship.

For males however, knowing if a member of our group is related to us is trickier. If we just arrived in a new group (because our own group kicked us out), we will share fewer genes with group members than a female would. To be as universally altruistic as females would thus often mean helping someone who is not a blood relative. The solution for that is not to be equally empathic with everyone. Now helping is only beneficial if we get help back, so we should just help those that have or will help us, and not those that have refused to help us in the past. The mechanism is then no longer helping to promote our own genes, but instead increases the chance of help in the future. Such a strategy takes a lot of brain power. We have to keep track of who is good and who is bad, and of who has helped us in the past. What is even more difficult is that, ideally, we should also help those that will help us tomorrow (even though we don't know that yet), because if they use the rule we use, they will not help us if they remember that we did not help them before. So not only do we have to keep track of who *did* help us, but we have to guess who *will* help us. It is therefore not surprising that those animals that really go out of their way to help other animals are not snails or frogs, but more intelligent social animals such as humans, apes, monkeys, dolphins, bats, and elephants. This is not because they are so smart that they are capable of rationally deciding what is good and what is bad, but because their brains allow them to recognize individuals and remember who did what.

Such gender differences, with males being more picky about whom they empathize with, is exactly what Tania Singer's experiment showed[69]. Seeing someone who has been generous to you get an electroshock makes you share his pain, potentially motivating help. Seeing someone who had been unfair to you get the same electroshock activates empathy in females but pleasure centers in males. Indeed, this gating of empathy through fairness seems not to be limited to humans. Apes will give food to other apes, but they will give more to those that have given them food in the past[xvi].

Now, helping someone only because they might or have helped you sounds very calculating. Is that really what goes through our head when we see the guy on the side of the road bleeding? Is that what goes through the head of the monkey when not pulling the chain? No, we simply share pain, and that drives us to help. The ultimate, evolutionary cause for a behavior is different from the proximal cause.

Generally put, it's emotions that set us in motion. Evolution manipulates these emotions to steer our behavior. We drink water, eat, sleep, and have sex because it feels good. The same applies to empathy and our moral sense. Monkeys and probably most humans do not refrain from hurting others because they calculate that this will make them more successful, but because it hurts to do so. In the split-second an ape has to decide whether to help defend a friend, he is unlikely to think about the future odds of reciprocation. He just feels a rush of sympathy and rage toward those whose actions bring about this shared pain. Emotions are calculations done by evolution.

In the eighties, political scientist Robert Axelrod and evolutionary biologist William D. Hamilton, both of Michigan University, teamed up to organize a contest. Each entry was a computer program that would play a game, the same prisoner's dilemma game that we encountered earlier in the context of Tania Singer's experiment, against other computer programs. In this game, each player decides whether to cooperate or defect. If both programs choose to cooperate, each gets 3 points. If one cooperates and the other defects, the former gets 0 and the latter 5 points. If both defect, they each get 1 point.

The game resembles many cases of human cooperation. If two partners cooperate in business, they do better than if each works alone, but they have to split the gain. If one puts his money into the business and the other runs away with it, one loses everything and the other wins everything without having to half the benefit. The challenge of the computer programmers was to find simple strategies to play these games.

Of all the many programs entered into the competition, the one that did best was the surprisingly simple "tit-for-tat" strategy. This program always cooperates on the first trial. If the opponent cooperates, it cooperates back, if the opponent defects, it defects back. This strategy did better than a strategy that always defects. Most surprisingly, tit-for-tat managed to do well even though many programs within the competition were rather evil and defected whenever they could. What this programmers challenge shows us is that even in the tough world of hostile computer-programs, a willingness to cooperate on the first encounter pays off, and a willingness to cooperate whenever someone has cooperated with you on the previous encounter will be an advantage.

Shared circuits and moral sentiments would therefore be a way to program our brain for this tit-for-tat strategy. Upon a first encounter, I shall share your feelings, and this will motivate me to help you. If you reciprocate, we will keep helping each other because it feels good to share the joy of those we help and bad to feel the pain of those we defect on. If you defect on me however, my feelings change, and I will no longer share your pain but strive to get revenge. This eye-for-an-eye instinct protects us against being suckered.

PSYCHOPATHY –THE DARK SIDE OF MORALITY

Psychopaths both fascinate and scare us. While we observe Hannibal Lector manipulate the FBI agent Clarice in the movie *Silence of the Lambs*, we cannot help but be mesmerized by the mixture of intelligence and cold blood that characterizes this Hollywood portrayal of a psychopath. At the same time we are tense and scared, because we feel that, despite the varnish of sophistication, Hannibal is capable of horrible crimes.

The likes of Hannibal Lector are intriguing. On the one hand, they seem to be cunning, Machiavellian human manipulators. On the other hand, the horrible crimes they commit without remorse suggest that they lack empathy. So, we have to wonder what really characterizes psychopathy, why they lack empathy and why the psychopath's social skills seem to be disconnected from their lacking empathy. Once we find that out, we could not only help protect society from dangerous psychopaths but also be on the way to better understanding morality and the peculiar selectivity of shared circuits for fair people.

A CHECKLIST TO IDENTIFY PSYCHOPATHS

Psychopaths do not exist only in Hollywood thrillers. A significant proportion of the criminals both inside and outside our prisons are psychopaths. Few of them perform the bizarre crimes of a Hannibal Lector, but most of them combine a talent for manipulation with a lack of remorse. Literally, the word *psychopathy* comes from *psyche*, "the mind," and *pathos*, "illness," but most mental health professionals reserve the term for people that do not lose contact with reality but nevertheless harm others without feeling guilt or empathy. The word sociopathy is often used as a synonym of psychopathy to emphasize the social dimension of this disorder.

Professional psychologists and psychiatrists have formalized the diagnosis of psychopathy over the last decades by developing a set of criteria that allows us to discriminate psychopaths from ordinary criminals and other individuals with psychiatric disorders. In particular, Robert D. Hare, Emeritus Professor of Psychology at the University of British Columbia, has devoted much of his career to developing the Psychopathy Checklist that allows clinicians worldwide to reliably diagnose and quantify psychopathy[138]. According to this checklist, the prototypical psychopath is characterized by a combination of four sets of traits, the last of which is a disturbing lack of empathy[xvii].

PSYCHOPATHS ARE GLIB AND GRANDIOSE LIARS

Psychopaths resemble the cliché of a dodgy used-car salesman. They speak glibly, but at the same time care very little about the truth. They can tell you a lie, and if you find them out they will switch to a new version without the slightest sign of embarrassment. They believe they are special and gifted, which gives them a sense of entitlement, a belief to have the right to take what they want and to be above the law.

One aspect that makes psychopaths so effective and fascinating is their capacity to charm and manipulate people. Psychopaths seem to intellectually detect very quickly what makes a person "tick," and will use this effectively. For instance, Ted Bundy, the American serial killer that confessed to killing twenty-nine women, lured his victims to him by walking around with superfluous crutches to make himself look harmless. Once he identified a woman who seemed keen to help him, he would drop his grocery bag next to his car and, when the woman rushed to help him pick it up, would hit her on the head with the very crutches that lead her to trust him, heave her into his car, and drive away to sexually abuse and kill her. The capacity of psychopaths to coldly engineer plans to manipulate people and use it to con a victim is their foremost talent.

SOCIOPATHS HAVE AN IMPULSIVE AND PARASITIC LIFESTYLE

Psychopaths also resemble small children in that they seem to lack the control most adults self-impose on their behavior. If a small child sees a stack of cookies, even if he knows that he should not eat them, the attraction will probably be stronger than its self control. If you later ask the child why it ate them, the answer will boil down to "because I felt like it." Sociopaths never grow out of this stage.

Sociopaths also fail to plan their future to achieve their goals. They may wish to be a pilot but will not plan the steps it takes to go to a flying academy and, instead, may fake the credentials and act as if they were pilots, swindling their way into the job, much as Leonardo di Caprio did in the movie *Catch Me If You Can*. They parasitically take what life offers. They will happily move in with a woman, let her pay all the bills and invest emotionally into a relationship, but they themselves will never feel the urge or obligation to reciprocate.

PSYCHOPATHS HAVE A HISTORY OF ANTISOCIAL BEHAVIOR

The past of the psychopath is littered with a history of behavior that harms other individuals and often starts in childhood. Children who become adult psychopaths often lie and cheat more than their peers. They steal, set fires, disrupt their classes, use drugs, and vandalize. They are often cruel to animals, much more so than other children their age.

As adults, psychopaths generally consider the rules and laws of society to be an inconvenient and unreasonable obstacle to their aspirations, and they behave as if these rules were not meant for them. As a result, most psychopaths will typically have a long list of convictions and, unlike most other prisoners that have a specialty (e.g., bank robbery), psychopaths typically have a mixed criminal history combining sexual offenses, theft, and violence. Some psychopaths seem to have enough control over their behavior to keep out of prison but will act in the gray zone of the law, being involved in dubious, reckless business activities, or emotionally harming their spouse and family members.

DON'T EMPATHIZE: THINK!

Why do psychopaths manipulate and harm others? Why do they ignore the rules and laws of society? I believe that the answer has something to do with shared circuits. Remember an episode in which you have caused distress, perhaps by bullying a weaker classmate, pulling the wings off an insect, or "dumping" a romantic partner. What do you feel? Most of us experience an unpleasant feeling that echoes the pain we have inflicted. What is important is that this aversive sensation makes us wish that we had acted otherwise and discourages us from repeating the misdeed. Indeed, an effective way to teach children not to harm others is to promote their empathic distress and draw their attention to the human suffering they have caused to others[139]. Based on this empathic sharing, most normal children quickly learn that violations of rules that harm people (e.g., don't hit people) are worse and fundamentally different from violations that do not (e.g., speaking with one's mouth full).

Psychopaths seem to be relatively insensitive to this process and can recall the damage they do to others with a frightening nonchalance. "The guy only had himself to blame," one of the inmates that Hare interviewed said of the man he had murdered in an argument about paying a bar tab. "Anybody could have seen I was in a rotten mood that night. What did he want to go and bother me for?" he continued. "Anyway, the guy never suffered. Knife wounds to an artery are the easiest way to go," [140][p41-42]. For them, hurting others seems as trivial a rule violation as speaking with a full mouth does to most of us. To them, murder is more like breaking a *conventional* rule than a *moral* rule, which is what sets psychopaths apart from us and non-psychopathic criminals. Although we are all capable of hurting other individuals, most of us will feel guilty about it. Psychopaths would not. "Guilt? . . . It's an illusion . . . and it's very unhealthy," Ted Bundy commented[141].

A psychopath's lack of sensitivity for distress is not just restricted to their perception of others. They speak of their own negative emotions in an abstract, hollow-sounding fashion as well, knowing the words, but not quite knowing what feelings are normally associated with them. Most of us, when we are frightened, experience a wealth of bodily feelings: our hands start sweating, our heart beats faster, our stomach contracts. In psychopaths, these physiological reactions are much less pronounced[142, 143]. "When I rob a bank, I notice that the teller shakes or becomes tongue-tied. One barfed all over the money. She must have been pretty messed up inside, but I don't know why,"[140][p54].

A psychopath's emotional experiences seem to be dominated by the basic motivations we would attribute to a lion, such as lust, hunger, and frustration, instead of the fear, anger, happiness, disgust, surprise, and sadness that are typical of most human adults' emotional lives.

KNOWING NO FEAR

In the context of shared circuits, it becomes striking that there might be a causal relationship between the emotional shallowness of psychopaths and their lack of empathy. As we have seen for the case of damage to the insula, being able to feel an emotion can be a necessary condition for empathizing with that emotion[54, 55]. If a psychopath does not experience distress as vividly as most of us do, his shared circuits lack the very voice they need to echo the distress of others.

One of Hare's interviewees, with a high score on the Psychopathy Checklist, very fittingly illustrated this link between feeling and empathizing: "[My victims] are frightened, right? But you see, I don't really understand it. I've been scared myself, and it wasn't unpleasant,"[140] [p44]. How can fear not be unpleasant? This psychopath clearly never experienced this emotion. He has learned to use the word "fear" in the appropriate context (e.g., when having a gun pointed at your head), but lacks the physiological and affective connotations that embody fear and make it so aversive to most of us. Accordingly, shared circuits in his brain have nothing to associate with the facial and behavioral display of his victims, and his victims' reactions remain a hollow and empty concept to him.

THE DARK ART OF SILENCING EMPATHIZING

Psychopaths are skilled at controlling and using other individuals. Unlike autistic individuals who find other people's minds mysterious, psychopaths seem to find it easy to think about the inner lives of others and use these thoughts to predict and to manipulate. Many sociopaths indeed mock their fellow humans by stating that the reason they take advantage of others is because it *is too easy* to manipulate them.

The fact that psychopaths however lack distress-related emotions and empathy for distress is conspicuously convenient because feeling distress or empathizing with the distress of others is punishing—and often gets in the way of achieving goals.

If an evil engineer in a science fiction movie were to design a perfect criminal he would probably create something capable of sharing and thinking about the actions, goals, needs, and feelings of others when it wants to, and at the same time equip it with the capacity to turn off its sharing of other people's emotions when that would be inconvenient, much like Data could switch its emotion chip on and off in *Star Trek, The Next Generation.* Now the creature could use its shared circuits and intelligence to manipulate others and shut off his feelings when they interfere with its criminal purpose. The capacity to con would then be free of the bounds of conscience, and a cold blooded but cunning psychopath would be born[140].

Most of us probably would probably love to have the ability to shut down emotions of fear and guilt –at least sometimes. But we can't. What makes us moral is not only our *capacity* to be empathic, but our *incapacity* to silence empathy. A creature designed for crime would differ in that it would sleep tight even after killing someone.

Of course, true psychopaths have not been designed by a diabolical engineer. This thought experiment, however, helps us understand how a combination of intelligence, shared circuits and the capacity to silence them when inconvenient would be a powerful combination that evolution could favor in order to create humans that thrive by exploitation. Seen from that perspective, we can only agree with one of the psychopaths in our studies that said, "I think my high psychopath score is a talent, not a sickness." The though experiment also illustrates a key potential difference between autism and psychopathy, which is that autistic individuals may have deficits in both their empathy and their capacity to think about the mind of others, whereas psychopaths may have the power to silence their empathy but their capacity for empathy and logically thought about the mind of others may be unaffected.

As we saw in Tania Singer's study, women shared pain as if vicarious suffering were an automatic process for them, but men seemed able to suppress this suffering whenever the other person had been unfair to them[129]. Many men also modulate their empathy based on hierarchical relationship. A top manager feels more empathy while firing a fellow manager than while laying off workman. This modulation may derive from the fact that peers are much more likely to be in a position to reciprocate. In this context, psychopaths' feelings of superiority may represent another extreme of a normal tendency not to be equally empathic toward all people, and the fact that psychopathy is more often observed in males than females also fits this idea[144].

A large scale twin study showed that, even at seven years of age, if one of two twins lacks empathy for distress, the other is far more likely also to lack this capacity if the two twins are identical (i.e., have the same genes) than if they are fraternal twins (and share only half of their genes). This suggests that the genes, and not the environment, which identical and fraternal twins share just as much, determine this psychopathic trait[142]. The existence of a genetic predisposition toward psychopathy unfortunately provides evolution with the means to select those that do best at suppressing the moral sentiments, allowing them to freely exploit others.

In collaboration with the Dutch department of Justice, my PhD student Harma Meffert, my wife Valeria, and I have started to investigate whether psychopaths activate their shared circuits less while witnessing the distress of others.

A DAY OUT FOR PATIENT 13

When Patient 13 wakes up this morning in the S. van Mesdag Clinic, a medieval looking fortress near Groningen, he finds out that today is the day. Over the last month, Harma Meffert had approached him several times in this high security forensic clinic to ask if he would be willing to participate in our experiment. Having been commited for a violent crime and having the maximum possible score (40) on the PCL-R, Patient 13 is exactly the kind of psychopath we want to scan. Something inside of him makes him hurt people without feeling guilt, and we want to find out what. Patient 13 enjoys the careful and polite way Harma now asks him if he is still willing to participate. Such a request for a favour makes him feel important; a welcome change from the orders he normally has to comply with. To prevent an escape plan, Patient 13 only knew he would be driven to our research center at some point, but not a precise day. An our after wakeup, Patient 13, with wooden rods in his trousers to prevent him from running away, now cumbursomely climbs out of the armoured Van into the back parking lot of our center. "I wish I had had more notice" he say, with a smile on his face. His smartly trimmed beard and hair and his coordinated close shows he likes to make a good impression on people. The three athletic gards at his side, wearing sweatshirts, look more like coaches than guards, and Patient 13 seems almost proud to have such an entourage. His escort does not wear guns: the wodden sticks in his trousers seem security enough. Metallic bullets would be dangerous in the vicinity of the fMRI scanner, and with the heavy door of the MRI scanner closing behind him, Patient 13 now has nowhere to run anyway. During the first half of the experiment, we measure his brain activity while he views movie clips in which the hands of two people interact. We told him simply to look at them carefully. In some of the movies, one hand hurts the other by twisting a finger. In others, the two hands lovingly caress each other. In others still, one hand seeks the other, but the other responds with a harsh, rejecting push away. Healthy control participants reported that seeing these movies triggers an empathic feeling: one of pain for the victim of the pain or the rejection, and one of warmth while watching the loving caress. The brains of these healthy participants also showed the activity in premotor, somatosensory and emotional brain regions we would expect if they shared what the actors in the movies were feeling. We want to know if the brain of psychopaths respond differently. Patient 13 is the thirteenth of 21 psychopathic individuals we measure in this way. He is polite, almost charming, but takes a sadistic pleasure in making us do what he wants. "Could I just go to the toilet one more time" he asks. Harma looks at the guards. They shrug. This means we lose another 20 minutes moving him in and out of the scanner, but we have no choice. As we take him out of the scanner, his constant smile still shows. He enjoys this reversal of roles: he orders and we all obay. In the second part of the experiment, after he is back from the bathroom, he gets to watch similar movies again, but this time, we ask him to try and feel with one of the hands in the movies, sometimes that of the victim, sometimes with that of the perpetrator. In the third part of the experiment, finally, Harma goes into the scanner room, and makes Patient 13 go through experiences similar to the ones in the movies. With his approval, she slaps his hand to make him feel light pain, pushes his hand away to make him feel rejected, and caresses him gently. After the experiment, most of the psychopath we scanned were unimpressed by the experiment: "it was stupid, boring", one of them later tells Alisson Abbott, my favorite reporter at the journal *Nature*. Psychopaths fail to see how our little movie clips have anything to do with the kind of brutal violence that is so unfortunately common in their lives. The experiment though turned out to be a success. During the first part of the experiment, while they were simply watching the movie clips, the psychopaths recruit the brain regions involved in performing their own actions and feeling their own sensations, pains and joys less, including SI, SII, the insula, and the premotor cortex, than age-matched control participants without psychopathy. Interestingly, although their brain activity in these regions was also slightly reduced while they felt similar states while Harma slapped or caressed them in the scanner, this difference in first hand experience was not as great as while they viewed the joys and pains of others. Our results therefore show that a lack of empathy for what other people do and feel indeed could be at the core of psychopathy. What is revealing, is that in contrast to the brain scans, the answers they gave in the Davis Interpersonal Reactivity Questionaire (see Annex) made them look like softhearted lambs, and as empathic as you and I. Psychopath are known to be cunning, responding to questionnaires whatever they believe will make their release more likely. Scanning their brains however reveals what their written answers conceil: deep inside, they silenced their empathy. But, as expected, our experiment reveals that they do not lack a capacity to empathize. In the second part of the experiment, in which we asked them to deliberately empathize with the people in the movies, their shared activity normalized, and was as strong as that of our controls. What distinguishes them from the controls is that they do not spontaneously empathize with others – not that they cannot empathize.

If our experiment seemed more revealing than questionnaires, why not use it in courtrooms to decide if a defendant is psychopathic or not? At present, this would be impossible. FMRI, is a very indirect measure of brain activity. As we saw in a previous chapter, neural activity changes blood flow which changes the magnetic field of the scanner a tiny little bit. Many factors beside the brain's response to our stimuli however also influences the FMRI measurement, including the temparature of the brain, breathing, head movements and even daydreaming. They all act as noise that often masks the real brain activity triggered by the stimuli in a single participant. Just like repeating the same words many time at a loud party finally makes them understandable, the noise in fMRI can be overcome by measuring the brain activity of many patients and averaging it. With fMRI we can then measure that the psychopathic brain is on average less empathic than ours, but we would be unable to say whether any single patient is psychopathic or not with the kind of confidence that a courtroom requires. Many research center, including the Netherlands Institute for Neuroscience in Amsterdam to which my team and I will move soon, therefore invest into newer generations of scanners that can measure brain activity with less noise. One of our goals with these newer scanners will be to diagnose mental disorders in single individuals. Till then, the PCL-R, based on criminal history and psychiatric assessments remains the most reliable instrument for assessing how psychopathic an individual is. FMRI experiments like ours, do not serve to diagnose patients but to give us insights into the mind of groups of patients that have already been diagnosed.

Therapies so far seem to have disappointingly little, if any, effect on the likelihood of a psychopath to committing further crimes after relase. Pharmaceuticals do not help at all, and psychopaths that received behavioral therapy actually seem to be even more likely to comit further crimes than those that have not. We hope that the finding that psychopaths do not lack the *capacity* to empathize but the propensity to do so spontaneously, might help focus new therapies. To help this progress, we are currently trying to develop animal models of empathy in order to learn more about how to influence shared circuits.

MORAL SHIELDS

Psychopaths' "talent" for silencing their empathy has a deep and destabilizing impact on society. If we were all equally empathic and our moral sentiments could never be ignored, all of us could freely and happily trust each other. The problem is that in such a world a mutation that would enable people to silence their empathy would have too easy a life. To protect ourselves from exploitation, we have grown moral shields, one of which is the law.

Our intuition tells us that hurting other people hurts us, but our laws and ethics institutionalize and reinforce this feeling. Just as all natural languages share certain universal features, all major religions, covering over 80 percent of the world's population, include the same basic Golden Rule. Each religion words this rule slightly differently. Jesus said, "In everything, do to others as you would have them do to you; for this is the law and the prophets" (Matthew 7:12); the Prophet Muhammad said, "Not one of you truly believes until you wish for others what you wish for yourself" (13th of the 40 Hadiths of Nawawi); Mahabharata reads, "This is the sum of duty: do not do to others what would cause pain if done to you" (Mahabharata 5:1517); Buddha said, "Treat not others in ways that you yourself would find hurtful" (Udana-Varga 5.1); and Hillel summarized the entire Torah as, "What is hateful to you, do not do to your neighbor. This is the whole Torah; all the rest is commentary. Go and learn it" (Talmud, Shabbath 31a). But all of these are almost uncanny in their sharing of the exact same core directive to treat others as you want to be treated.

The universality of certain rules of language tells us something about the brain, namely, that all human brains are wired in a way that makes languages that obey these rules easy to learn, and those that do not, hard[145]. The universality of empathy as a foundation of ethics and religious tells us something similar. The human brain is wired to be empathic and the fact that all these successful religions share the same golden rule is no coincidence. Because it reflects the working of our brain, religions that place it at their core are more easily acceptable and more compatible with our minds than ones that are not.

I SHALL DO TO YOU WHAT I WISH WOULD BE DONE TO ME

How nicely ethical laws dovetail with shared circuits becomes strikingly obvious in one important detail of the Golden Rule. The pattern of brain activity that results from shared circuits is not directly what happens to the other person, but what we would have felt in their place. We have seen that for actions in particular[19, 93]. As a result, shared circuits do not directly tell us the value the action has for the other, but instead makes us consider the value it would have for us in their place. We all know the effect this subtle point has on the result of our good-intentioned behavior. We are often tempted to give people what we personally long for, and are then sometimes disappointed to realize that they may have preferred something else.

This egocentric bias of shared circuits is strikingly captured in the Golden Rule of Ethics, which does not advise you to do to others what is good for *them*, but what you would wish *they would do for you.* The fact that so many wise men have formulated the rule in such a subjective way strengthens the idea that the Golden Rule is meant to build upon a preexisting neural mechanism that has the same properties: shared circuits.

LAWS EXIST BECAUSE OF CHEATERS AND PSYCHOPATHS

The golden rule also tells us something about the limitation of our intuitive ethics. If our brains were so deeply moral, why would we need explicit Golden Rules? The answer is complex. First, our shared circuits can be influenced by attention. If we actively avoid contemplating the negative consequences of our behavior, our shared circuits will have little evidence of pain for us to share. If we actively seek information about the consequences of our behavior, shared circuits will have more to share. One of the things the Golden Rule does is encourage us to attend to the social consequences of our behavior, which will enhance the influence of shared circuits and make us more ethical beings. By doing so, many religions encourage moral behavior and cooperation in their societies. The fact that over 80 percent of the world population now adheres to the Golden Rule makes our societies more successful and stable.

In addition, the Golden Rule does more than just draw people's attention to other people. In most societies, the Golden Rule has been transformed into Law, and officials such as judges and policemen will punish those that violate these laws.

Such punishment is sometimes essential, because if our own welfare depends on hurting others, we will have to neglect other people's points of view in favor of our own. A poor man stealing bread to feed his hungry children could feel the baker's distress, but will suppress it in the light of his children's' urgent needs. The competition for limited resources in a society creates exactly these conditions, and laws that discourage us from neglecting other people's needs by imposing punishment if we violate the interests of others ensures cohesion in real societies where shared circuits are seldom powerful enough.

Finally, psychopathy remains an important motor for ethical laws and punishment. There is a general tendency in evolution for every system to encourage a small proportion of cheaters that can make the entire system break down if they are not held in check. Most of us are ethical beings that respect the rights of other people. In this situation, psychopathic cheating becomes an amazingly profitable business. What would you do if a woman came to your door, asked you to donate a few dollars to help orphans in the third world, and showed you photographs of sad and hungry looking children? You will trust that person. You will feel empathy for the poor orphans, and will want to help them–after all, what are a couple of dollars for you compared to the week of food it can buy for them? You will thus donate some money. In many cases this money really does go to the orphans, but the ease with which people can obtain money using such a scheme means that, in some cases, the money will go straight into a con artist's pocket. This example is relatively benign, but imagine the impact a dishonest employee in a life insurance company can have. He could take the life savings of hundreds of hard working people and run away. If that happens often enough, people will stop trusting insurance companies, and soon the pension system and health insurance programs would collapse. Our market economies would rapidly decline and chaos would follow. Psychopaths are to ethical individuals what lions are to their prey. The lions can exist only because their prey exists, and yet they endanger the very species they feed upon. If psychopaths become too numerous, they jeopardize the very atmosphere of trust they rely on. Unfortunately, this will not only harm them, but also the honest humans that offer fairness for the benefits of collaboration. Biology tells us that cheating is unfortunately inevitable in a system and we thus have to accept that psychopathy is probably inevitable—an adaptation of a minority that exploits the benefits of ethics without paying their due.

Given that collaboration is key to the success of our species, two important mechanisms have evolved to keep the temptation of cheating in check. Genetic evolution has created a mechanism that makes us, at least men, enjoy punishing those that violate the Golden Rule[69]. This enjoyment could spontaneously motivate humans to punish cheaters, making cheating less profitable and thereby preserving the benefits of collaboration. Joseph Henrich of Emory University in Atlanta, together with an international team of scientists, has recently provided strong support for this idea. They examined fifteen different cultures, ranging from urban African, American, and Asian societies to isolated small-scale cultures in the tropical islands of Oceania, the rain forests of South America, and the African savannah. What they found was that, in all these cultures, individuals were ready to pay money to see an unfair person punished[146]. Such a universal readiness to punish unfair individuals strongly suggests that most humans around the globe share a genetic adaptation that serves to promote fair cooperation.

Second, in most societies, we do not only rely on common citizens to punish those that violate the Golden Rule. We appoint police officers and judges, and pay taxes to finance these institutions to ensure that a mighty force will punish those that violate our laws.

In ethical individuals, laws and altruistic punishment pull in the same direction as shared circuits. Together they help an intuitively ethical individual take the consequence his acts have for other people into account. For a psychopathic individual, the fear of punishment may be the only factor that prevents him from causing harm to other individuals. Laws can then be seen as the necessary means for stabilizing cooperation and protecting it against the predators of trust.

EPILOGUE:

ARE MIRROR NEURONS GOOD OR BAD?

When I started thinking about how we understand the social world around us, I envisioned a problem in which I am in here, in my brain and in my body, and you are all out there, in the world, beyond my immediate reach. How can I make sense of you? Understand you? My vision of human nature was typically western—that of a solipsistic individual.

The discovery of shared circuits changes the way we have to think about human nature. We are not strictly separated from the people around us. Many of the brain areas that were thought to be the strongholds of individuality turn out to be theatres of our social nature. The motor cortices in which we program what to do next, the theaters of free will and individual responsibility, turn out to mix our own will with the actions and intentions of others. The insulae, in which we sense the emotional state of our own body, also reflect the emotions of others as if they were as contagious as Influenza A. The somatosensory system, traditionally thought to be devoted to "proprioception," the perception of the self, represents the state of other people's body as well. In all these shared circuits, neurons that deal exclusively with the self coexist with neurons that respond similarly to self and other.

How much of us is purely private, then? How many of our bodily skills are ours? Shared circuits blur this question and distinction because the moment I see you do something, your actions become mine. The moment I see your pain, I share it. Are these actions and pain yours? Are they mine? The border between individuals is softened through the neural activity of these systems. A little bit of you becomes me, and a little bit of me becomes you.

Throughout this book I have tried to show how deeply shared circuits penetrate each and every aspect of our human social life, how they facilitate understanding, learning and language. What is more, we have seen how, given the basic capacity of our brain to learn associations through Hebbian processes ("what fires together, wires together") shared circuits seem to be an almost inevitable property of the human brain. We are deeply and inevitably social. Our societies, our culture, our knowledge, our technology, and our language—everything that makes us truly proud of being human seems to be a logical consequence of this brain architecture that makes us share each other's mind.

Linking mirror neurons and shared circuits to morality helps us understand the inner voice that tells us that hurting others is bad. Thinking that mirror neurons per se are either good or bad is too simplistic. Our decision to do an action or not is a balance between the benefit this act will have for ourselves and the vicarious consequences shared circuits make us feel. If we see the injured man on the side of the road, vicarious feelings motivate us to help even as the prospect of damage to our seats motivates us to drive onward. In that case, shared circuits motivate us to do the "right" thing, to help. A marketing man maximizing cigarette consumption by inducing the vicarious longing through the sight of the Marlboro Man lighting his cigarette while riding into the sunset uses shared circuits for a less noble cause. Apes using shared circuits to predict their prey's next move will kill a living being by using their mirror neurons. Mirror neurons are, like everything in nature, neither good nor bad.

The discovery of shared circuits has a profund impact on our understanding of morality. We now know that sharing the emotions of others is hardwired into our minds, and how this can be a foundation for our natural ethics and the core of ethical laws. Within the framework of evolution, the discovery of mirror neurons shows us that fairness and kinship are likely to influence the degree to which we empathize. We can understand why we care more about the guy around the corner than the faraway children of Africa. For our biology and our shared circuits, far from the eye means far from the heart.

Some might think this gives us permission not to care, and that it is moral because it is natural. But this is not the case. What *is* will never define what *ought* to be. Our brains were forged during an evolutionary process in which a faraway person could never reciprocate a favor. Now we live in worlds in which an intercontinental missile could annihilate every human life on the opposite side of the globe in only a couple of hours. The goal of neuroscience cannot be to tell us what is good or bad, but by making us understand the forces that govern our moral intuitions and sentiments, it can pinpoint the weaknesses and strength of what we are inclined to feel. By comparing these tendencies with what we, as a community, decide is good or bad will allow us to identify which laws might be more effective because they build on natural tendencies, and which might not. We can figure out where education will need more efforts. Neuroscientists can tell the people in NGOs that if they want people to donate more money to them, they have to trigger empathy by making us feel that the people of Africa are as close to us as the guy next door. Appealing to our rational thoughts is good, but appealing to our feelings might be more effective.

And one day, by charting the detailed machinery of empathy that the discovery of shared circuits has started to reveal, we might be in a position to understand and maybe even prevent the atrocities performed by the likes of Ted Bundy. The eighteenth century philosopher Immanuel Kant wrote in *Kritik der praktischen Vernunft*: "Two things fill the mind with ever new and increasing admiration and awe, the oftener and more steadily one reflects on them: the starry heavens above me and the moral law within me." We now know that his awe should have embraced the moral laws within our primate cousins as well. And yet, in our admiration of moral sentiments, of how "good" we are, we should not forget what we can see so clearly in monkeys and apes: that moral law and sentiment can coexist with brutal murder and violence.

Acknowledgements

Two people have been pivotal for this book: my wife and colleague, Valeria Gazzola, and my friend, Bas Kast. This book is ours.

Bas and I studied together. Together we passionately realised that understanding the brain is understanding who we are. This passion made him become what is probably Germany's most lucid and talented science writer. I became a scientist. His example is what inspired me to write. Throughout the writing of this book, his council and support gave me the stamina I needed. His editing transformed the first draft of this manuscript into a book worth reading.

Valeria and I founded the social brain lab together. Side-by-side, mind-by-mind and heart-by-heart we discovered what I describe in this book. Without her synergising passion, criticism and creativity, these years of research would not only have been so much lonelier - there would have generated so much less to write about. There is no greater gift for me than the privilege to share every second of my life with her. Our research told me that a human mind is not isolated. She makes me feel the reality of this conclusion day-by-day. All the illustrations in this book are hers.

I also wish to thank Anne Perrett for so patiently and genially polishing my English; Amanda Cushman, my editor at Dana Press, for shortening this book to pick up its pace; John Brockman and Katinka Matson, my agents, for believing in me. Finally, I thank the great scientists that have crossed and lit my path: Ruth Bennett, for guiding me along my first neuroscience efforts, David Perrett, my mentor, for showing me that science is not about the thrill of discovery but about integrity, creativity and honest curiosity; Vittorio Gallese and Giacomo Rizzolatti for inviting me into the wonderful world of mirror neurons, Bruno Wicker and Mel Goodale for introducing me to the world of fMRI and all the members, past and present, of our lab, for trusting me to be their mentors and contributing so much to understanding our social brain. The Marie Curie Program of the European

Comission and the Dutch Science Foundation (N.W.O.) have been absolutely critical for the work presented in this book by generously funding my research.

Finally, I wish to thank the person that told you about the existence of my book. In the old days, legacy publishers made sure the world knew about each book worth reading. In the days of independent writing, books remain unread unless readers talk, blog and post about them. So if you liked this book, please tell others about it.

Map of the Empathic Brain

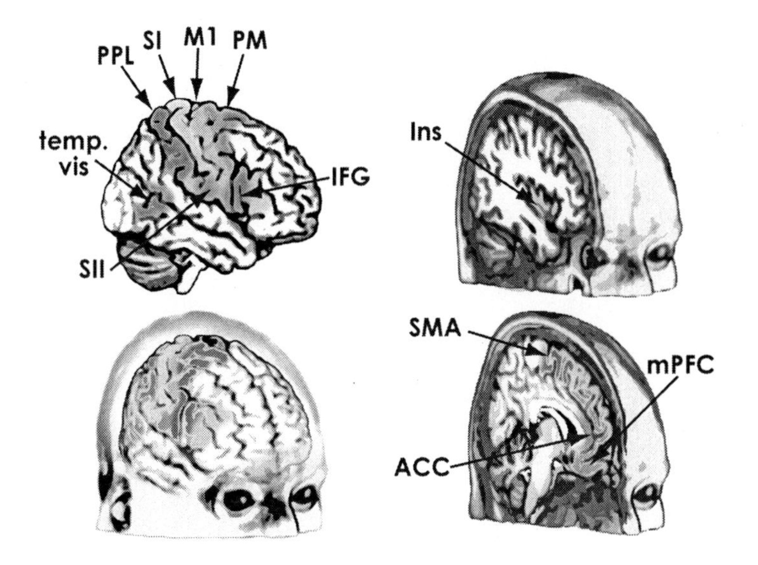

ACC (Anterior Cingulate Cortex): links emotions and actions

IFG (Inferior Frontal Gyrus): programs complex actions and language

Ins (Insula): senses the inner state of the body and controls visceral responses. Emotions

M1 (Primary motor cortex): controls muscles

mPFC (Medial PreFrontal Cortex): performs cognitive processing of the states of the self and of others

PM (PreMotor cortex): plans actions

PPL (Posterior Parietal Lobe): integrates information from all senses and programs responsive actions

SI/SII (Primary/Secondary Somatosensory Cortex): senses touch and the position of our own body (proprioception)

SMA (Supplementary Motor Area): plans and controls actions

V1 (Primary Visual cortex): detects simple features in the visual information from the retina

Temp.vis. (Temporal visual cortex): combines simple visual features detected by V1 and sometimes information from auditory cortices into neurons responding to the perception of socially relevant entities, e.g. faces, actions, etc.

Endnotes

i. A minority of philosophers and scientists had previously proposed that we understand the behavior of others by mapping it onto our own behavior but the discovery of mirror neurons was fundamental in showing that these proposals indeed apply to the brain.

ii. There are hundreds of experiments on the human mirror system. Choosing two for this book was difficult. Many other studies would certainly have merited inclusion if space had permitted. Amongst them, the following have had a particularly pioneering role: In 1995, Luciano Fadiga and colleagues (J. Neurophysiology 73, 2608-2611) showed that viewing an action increases the excitability of the primary motor cortex responsible for executing the same action. In 1996, Scott Grafton and collegues (Exp Brain Res 112, 103-111) showed that similar premotor and parietal areas are active during the execution of hand movements and during the sight of similar actions, in particular in the left hemisphere. In 1999, Marco Iacoboni and his colleagues (Science 286, 2526-2528) showed that action-observation and execution seem to interact in the ventral premotor cortex during imitation. In 2000, Marcel Brass and his colleagues (Brain Cogn 44, 124-143) could show that viewing a particular action accelerates the execution of the same and slows down the execution of an incompatible action.

iii. A detailed account of grammar would go beyond the scope of this book, but even to those that think that grammar was a boring and tedious part of school education, I recommend reading the exciting book *The Language Instinct* by Steven Pinker.

iv. The game is called prisoner's dilemma because of its original form. Two colleagues have just been convicted of a crime. In isolation cells, each convict is offered a deal: if he testifies against his colleague, but his colleague does not testify against him, he goes free but his friend will have to serve ten years. If nobody talks, both get six months because of insufficient evidence (cooperation mode), and if both testify, they both get five years. The predicament is that the convicts have to decide without knowing whether their colleague will talk.

v. Hebb did not actually use these words. Instead he stated "When an axon of cell A is near enough to excite cell B and repeatedly or persistently takes part in firing it, some growth process or metabolic change takes place in one or both cells such that A's efficiency, as one of the cells firing B, is increased".

vi. To illustrate the basic principle, I do not explicitly include the parietal cortex in this explanation, but the information always goes through the parietal cortex to reach F5.

vii. The idea that mirror neurons are not a system for understanding others, but the consequences of Hebbian learning in a system that primarily exists for controlling our own actions is similar to the ASL model of Cecilia Heyes (Trends Cogn Sci 5, 253-261).

viii. In engineering, the concept of predicting the sensory consequences of actions in order to check visual input has often been called 'forward modeling' (e.g. Neural Netw 9, 1265-1279)

ix. The experiment was conducted on 15 infants that viewed the actions first and 15 that experienced the Velcro mittens first. Alison and Anne are fictional characters that I invented for this description but they correspond to the average of each of the two sets of 15 infants.

x. I thank Marco del Giudice and Valeria Manera for drawing my attention to this experiment and helping me develop my thoughts on Hebbian learning.

xi. In their ASL model, Cecilia Heyes and Marcel Brass (Trends Cogn Sci 9, 489-495) nicely differentiate the two types of association: the association between the sound and the sight of actions are associations within the sensory domain, and are called 'horizontal' associations. Those between the sound and the execution of babbling cross representation levels and are called vertical.

xii. This mechanism does not require that the stimulus mirrors the child's behavior, even a system that emits a sound each time the child moves will attract the child's attention.

xiii. I will use the term autism as shorthand for the more accurate but cumbersome phrase 'autism spectrum disorders'. In cases where I want to refer to autism in the narrow sense, I will speak of autism proper.

xiv. Attunement refers to the sense of being in tune with someone else, empathically connected.

xv. This switching may involve a part of the brain that is known for playing a critical role when people switch their attention from one stimulus to another: the temporo-parietal junction (Mitchell, J.P. (2008) Cereb Cortex 18, 262-271)

xvi. Giving food is an indirect process in apes: rather than truly giving food, they tolerate the fact that another ape eats some of theirs.

xvii. In his book Without Conscience,Robert Hare provides a very rich description of psychopaths, full of quotes that illustrate the psychopathic way of thinking.

Bibliography

All publications of the social brain laboratory can be found on our web page: http://www.nin.knaw.nl/research_groups/keysers_group.

1. Graziano, M.S., Taylor, C.S., and Moore, T. (2002). Complex movements evoked by microstimulation of precentral cortex. Neuron *34*, 841-851.
2. Fried, I., Katz, A., McCarthy, G., Sass, K.J., Williamson, P., Spencer, S.S., and Spencer, D.D. (1991). Functional organization of human supplementary motor cortex studied by electrical stimulation. J Neurosci *11*, 3656-3666.
3. Umilta, M.A., Kohler, E., Gallese, V., Fogassi, L., Fadiga, L., Keysers, C., and Rizzolatti, G. (2001). I know what you are doing. a neurophysiological study. Neuron *31*, 155-165.
4. Fadiga, L., Fogassi, L., Pavesi, G., and Rizzolatti, G. (1995). Motor facilitation during action observation: a magnetic stimulation study. J Neurophysiol *73*, 2608-2611.
5. Grafton, S.T., Arbib, M.A., Fadiga, L., and Rizzolatti, G. (1996). Localization of grasp representations in humans by positron emission tomography. 2. Observation compared with imagination. Exp Brain Res *112*, 103-111.
6. Iacoboni, M., Woods, R.P., Brass, M., Bekkering, H., Mazziotta, J.C., and Rizzolatti, G. (1999). Cortical mechanisms of human imitation. Science *286*, 2526-2528.
7. Brass, M., Bekkering, H., Wohlschlager, A., and Prinz, W. (2000). Compatibility between observed and executed finger movements: comparing symbolic, spatial, and imitative cues. Brain Cogn *44*, 124-143.
8. Aziz-Zadeh, L., Iacoboni, M., Zaidel, E., Wilson, S., and Mazziotta, J. (2004). Left hemisphere motor facilitation in response to manual action sounds. Eur J Neurosci *19*, 2609-2612.
9. Gazzola, V., Aziz-Zadeh, L., and Keysers, C. (2006). Empathy and the somatotopic auditory mirror system in humans. Curr Biol *16*, 1824-1829.
10. Mukamel, R., Ekstrom, A.D., Kaplan, J., Iacoboni, M., and Fried, I. (2010). Single-Neuron Responses in Humans during Execution and Observation of Actions. Curr Biol.
11. Keysers, C., and Gazzola, V. (2010). Social Neuroscience: Mirror Neurons Recorded in Humans. Current Biology *20*, R353-R354.
12. Hietanen, J.K., and Perrett, D.I. (1993). Motion sensitive cells in the macaque superior temporal polysensory area. I. Lack of response to the sight of the

animal's own limb movement. Exp Brain Res *93*, 117-128.

13. Blakemore, S.J., Frith, C.D., and Wolpert, D.M. (1999). Spatio-temporal prediction modulates the perception of self-produced stimuli. J Cogn Neurosci *11*, 551-559.
14. Davis, M.H. (1980). A multidimensional approach to individual differences in empathy. Catalog of Selected Documents in Psychology *10*, 1.
15. Davis, M.H. (1983). Measuring individual differences in empathy: Evidence for a multidimensional approach. Journal of Personality and Social Psychology *44*, 113-126.
16. Desimone, R. (1998). Visual attention mediated by biased competition in extrastriate visual cortex. Philos Trans R Soc Lond B Biol Sci *353*, 1245-1255.
17. Bangert, M., Peschel, T., Schlaug, G., Rotte, M., Drescher, D., Hinrichs, H., Heinze, H.J., and Altenmuller, E. (2006). Shared networks for auditory and motor processing in professional pianists: evidence from fMRI conjunction. Neuroimage *30*, 917-926.
18. Calvo-Merino, B., Grezes, J., Glaser, D.E., Passingham, R.E., and Haggard, P. (2006). Seeing or doing? Influence of visual and motor familiarity in action observation. Curr Biol *16*, 1905-1910.
19. Gazzola, V., Rizzolatti, G., Wicker, B., and Keysers, C. (2007). The anthropomorphic brain: the mirror neuron system responds to human and robotic actions. Neuroimage *35*, 1674-1684.
20. Buccino, G., Lui, F., Canessa, N., Patteri, I., Lagravinese, G., Benuzzi, F., Porro, C.A., and Rizzolatti, G. (2004). Neural circuits involved in the recognition of actions performed by nonconspecifics: an FMRI study. J Cogn Neurosci *16*, 114-126.
21. Rijntjes, M., Dettmers, C., Buchel, C., Kiebel, S., Frackowiak, R.S., and Weiller, C. (1999). A blueprint for movement: functional and anatomical representations in the human motor system. J Neurosci *19*, 8043-8048.
22. Meltzoff, A.N., and Moore, M.K. (1977). Imitation of facial and manual gestures by human neonates. Science *198*, 74-78.
23. Thorpe, W. (1956). Learning and instict in animals, (London: Methuen).
24. Gallese, V., Fadiga, L., Fogassi, L., and Rizzolatti, G. (1996). Action recognition in the premotor cortex. Brain *119 (Pt 2)*, 593-609.
25. Subiaul, F., Cantlon, J.F., Holloway, R.L., and Terrace, H.S. (2004). Cognitive imitation in rhesus macaques. Science *305*, 407-410.
26. Jabbi, M., Bastiaansen, J., and Keysers, C. (2008). A common anterior insula representation of disgust observation, experience and imagination shows divergent functional connectivity pathways. PLoS ONE *3*, e2939.

27. Jacob, F. (1977). Evolution and tinkering. Science *196*, 1161-1166.

28. Central-Intelligence-Agency (2008). The 2008 World Factbook, (Directorate of Intelligence).

29. Pinker, S. (1994). The language instinct, (London: The Pinguin Press).

30. Senghas, A., Kita, S., and Ozyurek, A. (2004). Children creating core properties of language: evidence from an emerging sign language in Nicaragua. Science *305*, 1779-1782.

31. Chomsky, N. (1965). Aspects of the theory of syntax, (Cambridge, Mass: MIT press).

32. Shubin, N. (2008). Your Inner Fish, (New York: Patheon Books).

33. Csibra, G., and Gergely, G. (2009). Natural pedagogy. Trends Cogn Sci *13*, 148-153.

34. Vargha-Khadem, F., Gadian, D.G., Copp, A., and Mishkin, M. (2005). FOXP2 and the neuroanatomy of speech and language. Nat Rev Neurosci *6*, 131-138.

35. Watkins, K.E., Dronkers, N.F., and Vargha-Khadem, F. (2002). Behavioural analysis of an inherited speech and language disorder: comparison with acquired aphasia. Brain *125*, 452-464.

36. Bookheimer, S. (2002). Functional MRI of language: new approaches to understanding the cortical organization of semantic processing. Annu Rev Neurosci *25*, 151-188.

37. Marshall-Pescini, S., and Whiten, A. (2008). Social learning of nut-cracking behavior in East African sanctuary-living chimpanzees (Pan troglodytes schweinfurthii). J Comp Psychol *122*, 186-194.

38. Wilson, S.M., Saygin, A.P., Sereno, M.I., and Iacoboni, M. (2004). Listening to speech activates motor areas involved in speech production. Nat Neurosci *7*, 701-702.

39. Keysers, C., Kohler, E., Umilta, M.A., Nanetti, L., Fogassi, L., and Gallese, V. (2003). Audiovisual mirror neurons and action recognition. Exp Brain Res *153*, 628-636.

40. Kohler, E., Keysers, C., Umilta, M.A., Fogassi, L., Gallese, V., and Rizzolatti, G. (2002). Hearing sounds, understanding actions: action representation in mirror neurons. Science *297*, 846-848.

41. Fadiga, L., Craighero, L., Buccino, G., and Rizzolatti, G. (2002). Speech listening specifically modulates the excitability of tongue muscles: a TMS study. Eur J Neurosci *15*, 399-402.

42. Meister, I.G., Wilson, S.M., Deblieck, C., Wu, A.D., and Iacoboni, M. (2007). The essential role of premotor cortex in speech perception. Curr Biol *17*, 1692-1696.

43. Kuhl, P.K., and Miller, J.D. (1975). Speech perception by the chinchilla: voiced-voiceless distinction in alveolar plosive consonants. Science *190*, 69-72.
44. Hauk, O., Johnsrude, I., and Pulvermuller, F. (2004). Somatotopic representation of action words in human motor and premotor cortex. Neuron *41*, 301-307.
45. Rizzolatti, G., Camarda, R., Fogassi, L., Gentilucci, M., Luppino, G., and Matelli, M. (1988). Functional organization of inferior area 6 in the macaque monkey. II. Area F5 and the control of distal movements. Exp Brain Res *71*, 491-507.
46. Damasio, A.R. (2003). Looking for Spinoza: Joy, Sorrow and the Feeling Brain, (New York, New York: Hartcourt).
47. Hatfield, E., Cacioppo, J.T., and Rapson, R.L. (1993). Emotional contagion, (New York: Cambridge university press).
48. James, W. (1884). What is an Emotion. Mind *9*, 188-205.
49. Rogers, C.R. (1957). The necessary and sufficient conditions of therapeutic personality change. J. Consult. Psychol. *21*, 95-103.
50. Penfield, W., and Faulk, M.E., Jr. (1955). The insula; further observations on its function. Brain *78*, 445-470.
51. Wicker, B., Keysers, C., Plailly, J., Royet, J.P., Gallese, V., and Rizzolatti, G. (2003). Both of us disgusted in My insula: the common neural basis of seeing and feeling disgust. Neuron *40*, 655-664.
52. Keysers, C., and Gazzola, V. (2006). Towards a unifying neural theory of social cognition. Prog Brain Res *156*, 379-401.
53. Keysers, C., and Gazzola, V. (2009). Expanding the mirror: vicarious activity for actions, emotions, and sensations. Curr Opin Neurobiol *19*, 666-671.
54. Calder, A.J., Keane, J., Manes, F., Antoun, N., and Young, A.W. (2000). Impaired recognition and experience of disgust following brain injury. Nat Neurosci *3*, 1077-1078.
55. Adolphs, R., Tranel, D., and Damasio, A.R. (2003). Dissociable neural systems for recognizing emotions. Brain Cogn *52*, 61-69.
56. Adolphs, R., Tranel, D., Koenigs, M., and Damasio, A.R. (2005). Preferring one taste over another without recognizing either. Nat Neurosci *8*, 860-861.
57. Mesulam, M.M., and Mufson, E.J. (1982). Insula of the old world monkey. III: Efferent cortical output and comments on function. J Comp Neurol *212*, 38-52.
58. Singer, T., Seymour, B., O'Doherty, J., Kaube, H., Dolan, R.J., and Frith, C.D. (2004). Empathy for pain involves the affective but not sensory components of pain. Science *303*, 1157-1162.

59. Jabbi, M., Swart, M., and Keysers, C. (2007). Empathy for positive and negative emotions in the gustatory cortex. Neuroimage *34*, 1744-1753.

60. Morecraft, R.J., Stilwell-Morecraft, K.S., and Rossing, W.R. (2004). The motor cortex and facial expression: new insights from neuroscience. Neurologist *10*, 235-249.

61. van der Gaag, C., Minderaa, R., and Keysers, C. (2007). Facial expressions: what the mirror neuron system can and cannot tell us. Social Neuroscience *2*, 179-222.

62. Adolphs, R., Damasio, H., Tranel, D., Cooper, G., and Damasio, A.R. (2000). A role for somatosensory cortices in the visual recognition of emotion as revealed by three-dimensional lesion mapping. J Neurosci *20*, 2683-2690.

63. Beilock, S.L., and Holt, L.E. (2007). Embodied preference judgments: can likeability be driven by the motor system? Psychol Sci *18*, 51-57.

64. Jabbi, M., and Keysers, C. (2008). Inferior frontal gyrus activity triggers anterior insula response to emotional facial expressions. Emotion *8*, 775-780.

65. Lanzetta, J.T., and Englis, B.G. (1989). Expectations of cooperation and competition and their effects on observers' vicarious emotional responses. J. Pers. Soc. Psychol. *56*, 543-554.

66. Hess, U., and Blairy, S. (2001). Facial mimicry and emotional contagion to dynamic emotional facial expressions and their influence on decoding accuracy. Int J Psychophysiol *40*, 129-141.

67. Smith, A. (1759). The Theory of the Moral Sentiments. (Adam Smith Institute).

68. Banissy, M.J., and Ward, J. (2007). Mirror-touch synesthesia is linked with empathy. Nat Neurosci *10*, 815-816.

69. Singer, T., Seymour, B., O'Doherty, J.P., Stephan, K.E., Dolan, R.J., and Frith, C.D. (2006). Empathic neural responses are modulated by the perceived fairness of others. Nature *439*, 466-469.

70. Gilligan, C. (1982). In a different voice, (Cambridge: Harvard University Press).

71. Gazzola, V., and Keysers, C. (2009). The observation and execution of actions share motor and somatosensory voxels in all tested subjects: single-subject analyses of unsmoothed fMRI data. Cereb Cortex *19*, 1239-1255.

72. Keysers, C., Kaas, J.H., and Gazzola, V. (2010). Somatosensation in social perception. Nat Rev Neurosci *11*, 417-428.

73. Hebb, D. (1949). The organisation of behaviour, (Wiley).

74. Bi, G., and Poo, M. (2001). Synaptic modification by correlated activity: Hebb's postulate revisited. Annu Rev Neurosci *24*, 139-166.

75. Stent, G.S. (1973). A physiological mechanism for Hebb's postulate of learning. Proc Natl Acad Sci U S A *70*, 997-1001.
76. Keysers, C., and Perrett, D.I. (2004). Demystifying social cognition: a Hebbian perspective. Trends Cogn Sci *8*, 501-507.
77. Heyes, C. (2001). Causes and consequences of imitation. Trends Cogn Sci *5*, 253-261.
78. Perrett, D.I., Oram, M.W., Harries, M.H., Bevan, R., Hietanen, J.K., Benson, P.J., and Thomas, S. (1991). Viewer-centred and object-centred coding of heads in the macaque temporal cortex. Exp Brain Res *86*, 159-173.
79. von Hofsten, C. (2004). An action perspective on motor development. Trends Cogn Sci *8*, 266-272.
80. Brass, M., and Heyes, C. (2005). Imitation: is cognitive neuroscience solving the correspondence problem? Trends Cogn Sci *9*, 489-495.
81. Blakemore, S.J., Wolpert, D., and Frith, C. (2000). Why can't you tickle yourself? Neuroreport *11*, R11-16.
82. Wolpert, D.M., and Miall, R.C. (1996). Forward Models for Physiological Motor Control. Neural Netw *9*, 1265-1279.
83. Sommerville, J.A., Woodward, A.L., and Needham, A. (2005). Action experience alters 3-month-old infants' perception of others' actions. Cognition *96*, B1-11.
84. Woodward, A.L. (1998). Infants selectively encode the goal object of an actor's reach. Cognition *69*, 1-34.
85. Barraclough, N.E., Xiao, D., Baker, C.I., Oram, M.W., and Perrett, D.I. (2005). Integration of visual and auditory information by superior temporal sulcus neurons responsive to the sight of actions. J Cogn Neurosci *17*, 377-391.
86. Keysers, C., Wicker, B., Gazzola, V., Anton, J.L., Fogassi, L., and Gallese, V. (2004). A touching sight: SII/PV activation during the observation and experience of touch. Neuron *42*, 335-346.
87. Blakemore, S.J., Bristow, D., Bird, G., Frith, C., and Ward, J. (2005). Somatosensory activations during the observation of touch and a case of vision-touch synaesthesia. Brain *128*, 1571-1583.
88. Botvinick, M., and Cohen, J. (1998). Rubber hands 'feel' touch that eyes see. Nature *391*, 756.
89. Meltzoff, A.N., and Borton, R.W. (1979). Intermodal matching by human neonates. Nature *282*, 403-404.
90. Anisfeld, M. (1996). Only tongue protrusion modeling is matched by neonates. Developmental Review *16*, 149-161.
91. Ekman, P., Sorenson, E.R., and Friesen, W.V. (1969). Pan-cultural elements in

facial displays of emotion. Science *164*, 86-88.

92. Tarabulsy, G.M., Tessier, R., and Kappas, A. (1996). Contingency detection and the contingent organization of behavior in interactions: implications for socioemotional development in infancy. Psychol Bull *120*, 25-41.
93. Gazzola, V., van der Worp, H., Mulder, T., Wicker, B., Rizzolatti, G., and Keysers, C. (2007). Aplasics Born without Hands Mirror the Goal of Hand Actions with Their Feet. Curr Biol *17*, 1235-1240.
94. Lahav, A., Saltzman, E., and Schlaug, G. (2007). Action Representation of Sound: Audiomotor Recognition Network While Listening to Newly Acquired Actions. J. Neurosci. *27*, 308-314.
95. Thioux, M., Stark, D.E., Klaiman, C., and Schultz, R.T. (2006). The day of the week when you were born in 700 ms: calendar computation in an Autistic savant. J Exp Psychol Hum Percept Perform *32*, 1155-1168.
96. Klin, A., Jones, W., Schultz, R., Volkmar, F., and Cohen, D. (2002). Visual fixation patterns during viewing of naturalistic social situations as predictors of social competence in individuals with autism. Arch Gen Psychiatry *59*, 809-816.
97. Dapretto, M., Davies, M.S., Pfeifer, J.H., Scott, A.A., Sigman, M., Bookheimer, S.Y., and Iacoboni, M. (2006). Understanding emotions in others: mirror neuron dysfunction in children with autism spectrum disorders. Nat Neurosci *9*, 28-30.
98. Iacoboni, M., and Dapretto, M. (2006). The mirror neuron system and the consequences of its dysfunction. Nat Rev Neurosci *7*, 942-951.
99. Oberman, L.M., Hubbard, E.M., McCleery, J.P., Altschuler, E.L., Ramachandran, V.S., and Pineda, J.A. (2005). EEG evidence for mirror neuron dysfunction in autism spectrum disorders. Brain Res Cogn Brain Res *24*, 190-198.
100. Williams, J.H., Waiter, G.D., Gilchrist, A., Perrett, D.I., Murray, A.D., and Whiten, A. (2006). Neural mechanisms of imitation and 'mirror neuron' functioning in autistic spectrum disorder. Neuropsychologia *44*, 610-621.
101. Williams, J.H., Whiten, A., and Singh, T. (2004). A systematic review of action imitation in autistic spectrum disorder. J Autism Dev Disord *34*, 285-299.
102. Avikainen, S., Wohlschlager, A., Liuhanen, S., Hanninen, R., and Hari, R. (2003). Impaired mirror-image imitation in Asperger and high-functioning autistic subjects. Curr Biol *13*, 339-341.
103. Hamilton, A.F., Brindley, R.M., and Frith, U. (2007). Imitation and action understanding in autistic spectrum disorders: how valid is the hypothesis of a deficit in the mirror neuron system? Neuropsychologia *45*, 1859-1868.

104. McIntosh, D.N., Reichmann-Decker, A., Winkielman, P., and Wilbarger, J.L. (2006). When the social mirror breaks: deficits in automatic, but not voluntary, mimicry of emotional facial expressions in autism. Developmental Science *9*, 295-302.

105. Bekkering, H., Wohlschlager, A., and Gattis, M. (2000). Imitation of gestures in children is goal-directed. Q J Exp Psychol A *53*, 153-164.

106. Rogers, S.J., Bennetto, L., McEvoy, R., and Pennington, B.F. (1996). Imitation and pantomime in high-functioning adolescents with autism spectrum disorders. Child Dev *67*, 2060-2073.

107. Vanvuchelen, M., Roeyers, H., and De Weerdt, W. (2007). Nature of motor imitation problems in school-aged boys with autism: A motor or a cognitive problem? Autism *11*, 225-240.

108. Vanvuchelen, M., Roeyers, H., and De Weerdt, W. (2007). Nature of motor imitation problems in school-aged males with autism: how congruent are the error types? Dev Med Child Neurol *49*, 6-12.

109. Avikainen, S., Kulomaki, T., and Hari, R. (1999). Normal movement reading in Asperger subjects. Neuroreport *10*, 3467-3470.

110. Dinstein, I., Thomas, C., Humphreys, K., Minshew, N., Behrmann, M., and Heeger, D.J. (2010). Normal movement selectivity in autism. Neuron *66*, 461-469.

111. Bastiaansen, J.A., Thioux, M., Nanetti, L., van der Gaag, C., Ketelaars, C., Minderaa, R., and Keysers, C. (2011). Age-Related Increase in Inferior Frontal Gyrus Activity and Social Functioning in Autism Spectrum Disorder. Biol Psychiatry.

112. Sudhof, T.C. (2008). Neuroligins and neurexins link synaptic function to cognitive disease. Nature *455*, 903-911.

113. Cherkassky, V.L., Kana, R.K., Keller, T.A., and Just, M.A. (2006). Functional connectivity in a baseline resting-state network in autism. Neuroreport *17*, 1687-1690.

114. Just, M.A., Cherkassky, V.L., Keller, T.A., Kana, R.K., and Minshew, N.J. (2007). Functional and anatomical cortical underconnectivity in autism: evidence from an FMRI study of an executive function task and corpus callosum morphometry. Cereb Cortex *17*, 951-961.

115. Courchesne, E., Karns, C.M., Davis, H.R., Ziccardi, R., Carper, R.A., Tigue, Z.D., Chisum, H.J., Moses, P., Pierce, K., Lord, C., et al. (2001). Unusual brain growth patterns in early life in patients with autistic disorder: An MRI study. Neurology *57*, 245-254.

116. Kuhl, P.K., Coffey-Corina, S., Padden, D., and Dawson, G. (2005). Links be-

tween social and linguistic processing of speech in preschool children with autism: behavioral and electrophysiological measures. Dev Sci *8*, F1-F12.

117. Adolphs, R., and Spezio, M. (2006). Role of the amygdala in processing visual social stimuli. Prog Brain Res *156*, 363-378.
118. Ingersoll, B., and Schreibman, L. (2006). Teaching reciprocal imitation skills to young children with autism using a naturalistic behavioral approach: effects on language, pretend play, and joint attention. J Autism Dev Disord *36*, 487-505.
119. Ingersoll, B., and Gergans, S. (2007). The effect of a parent-implemented imitation intervention on spontaneous imitation skills in young children with autism. Res Dev Disabil *28*, 163-175.
120. Kast, B. (2006). Die Liebe und wie sich Leidenschaft erklärt, (Fischer).
121. Buss, D.M., and Barnes, M. (1986). PREFERENCES IN HUMAN MATE SELECTION. Journal of Personality and Social Psychology *50*, 559-570.
122. Weisfeld, G.E., Russell, R.J.H., Weisfeld, C.C., and Wells, P.A. (1992). CORRELATES OF SATISFACTION IN BRITISH MARRIAGES. Ethology and Sociobiology *13*, 125-145.
123. Ferrari, P.F., Gallese, V., Rizzolatti, G., and Fogassi, L. (2003). Mirror neurons responding to the observation of ingestive and communicative mouth actions in the monkey ventral premotor cortex. Eur J Neurosci *17*, 1703-1714.
124. Keysers, C., and Gazzola, V. (2007). Integrating simulation and theory of mind: from self to social cognition. Trends Cogn Sci *11*, 194-196.
125. Critchley, H.D., Wiens, S., Rotshtein, P., Ohman, A., and Dolan, R.J. (2004). Neural systems supporting interoceptive awareness. Nat Neurosci *7*, 189-195.
126. Berthoz, S., Artiges, E., Van De Moortele, P.F., Poline, J.B., Rouquette, S., Consoli, S.M., and Martinot, J.L. (2002). Effect of impaired recognition and expression of emotions on frontocingulate cortices: an fMRI study of men with alexithymia. Am J Psychiatry *159*, 961-967.
127. Mitchell, J.P., Macrae, C.N., and Banaji, M.R. (2006). Dissociable medial prefrontal contributions to judgments of similar and dissimilar others. Neuron *50*, 655-663.
128. Mitchell, J.P. (2007). Activity in Right Temporo-Parietal Junction is Not Selective for Theory-of-Mind. Cereb Cortex.
129. Singer, T. (2006). The neuronal basis and ontogeny of empathy and mind reading: review of literature and implications for future research. Neurosci Biobehav Rev *30*, 855-863.
130. Feinman, S., Roberts, D., Hsieh, K.F., Sawyer, D., and Swanson, K. (1992). A critical review of social referencing in infancy. In Social Referencing and the Social Construction of Reality in Infancy, S. Feinman, ed. (New York: Plenum

Press).

131. Perner, J., Leekam, S.R., and Wimmer, H. (1987). 2-Year-Olds Difficulty with False Belief - the Case for a Conceptual Deficit. British Journal of Developmental Psychology *5*, 125-137.
132. Baroncohen, S., Leslie, A.M., and Frith, U. (1985). Does the Autistic-Child Have a Theory of Mind. Cognition *21*, 37-46.
133. Kast, B. (2007). Wie der Bauch dem Kopf beim Denken Hilft, (Berlin: Fischer Verlag).
134. Aziz-Zadeh, L., Wilson, S.M., Rizzolatti, G., and Iacoboni, M. (2006). Congruent embodied representations for visually presented actions and linguistic phrases describing actions. Curr Biol *16*, 1818-1823.
135. Haidt, J. (2001). The emotional dog and its rational tail: a social intuitionist approach to moral judgment. Psychol Rev *108*, 814-834.
136. Greene, J.D., Nystrom, L.E., Engell, A.D., Darley, J.M., and Cohen, J.D. (2004). The neural bases of cognitive conflict and control in moral judgment. Neuron *44*, 389-400.
137. Masserman, J.H., Wechkin, S., and Terris, W. (1964). "Altruistic" Behavior in Rhesus Monkeys. Am J Psychiatry *121*, 584-585.
138. Hare, R.D. (2003). Manual for the Hare Psychopathy Checklist-Revisited, 2nd ed, (Toronto: Multi-Health Systems).
139. Hoffman, M.L. (1994). Discipline and Internalization. Developmental Psychology *30*, 26-28.
140. Hare, R.D. (1993). Without Conscience: The Disturbing World of the Psychopath Amongst Us., (New York: Pocket Books).
141. Michaud, S.G., and Aynesworth, H. (1989). Ted Bundy: Conversations with a Killer, (New York: New American Library).
142. Blair, R.J. (2006). The emergence of psychopathy: implications for the neuropsychological approach to developmental disorders. Cognition *101*, 414-442.
143. Kiehl, K.A. (2006). A cognitive neuroscience perspective on psychopathy: evidence for paralimbic system dysfunction. Psychiatry Res *142*, 107-128.
144. Dolan, M., and V^llm, B. Antisocial personality disorder and psychopathy in women: A literature review on the reliability and validity of assessment instruments. International Journal of Law and Psychiatry *32*, 2-9.
145. Chomsky, N. (1959). VERBAL-BEHAVIOR - SKINNER,BF. Language *35*, 26-58.
146. Henrich, J., McElreath, R., Barr, A., Ensminger, J., Barrett, C., Bolyanatz, A., Cardenas, J.C., Gurven, M., Gwako, E., Henrich, N., et al. (2006). Costly punishment across human societies. Science *312*, 1767-1770.

ABOUT THE AUTHOR

Dr. Christian Keysers' work on mirror neurons and how the brain allows us to share the inner state of others has been seminal for the scientific study of empathy. Of French and German nationality, he was born in 1973 and has worked and lived in five European countries and the US. His work has led to publications in the most prominent scientific journals and has made him one of the youngest people to attain the rank of Full Professor. His capacity to explain his science to the wider audience earned him the Marie Curie Excellence Award. He now fulfills his dream to dedicate his life to research by leading a laboratory together with his wife at the Netherlands Institute for Neuroscience (www.nin.knaw.nl), a research institute of the Royal Dutch Academy of Arts and Sciences in Amsterdam. He is also a Full Professor at the University Medical Center Groningen in the Netherlands and a frequent Visiting Professor at the California Institute of Technology. Outside of the laboratory, his wife Valeria and his daughter Julia are teaching him why empathy is such a gift.

If you want to contact him, please email christian.keysers@gmail.com, or post a message on the wall of facebook.com/theempathicbrain.

If you liked this book, please tell your friends about it. For independent author, the word of mouth is the best way for a book to reach its audience.

Finally, if you are excited about the research on empathy, and would like to support it, the social brain lab always needs help: you can join the team if you are a scientist, or you can endowed doctoral or postdoctoral positions if you are one of the fortunate people that have the means to do so.

APPENDIX:

THE DAVIS INTERPERSONAL REACTIVITY INDEX

The following statements inquire about your thoughts and feelings in a variety of situations. For each item, indicate how well it describes you by choosing the appropriate letter on the scale at the top of the page: A, B, C, D, or E. When you have decided on your answer, write it down on a separate sheet of paper together with the number of the item. Read each item carefully before responding. Answer as honestly as you can. For now, ignore the letters and minus sign in brackets next to the items. They will serve later for scoring the scale.

ANSWER SCALE:

A	B	C	D	E
Does not describe me well				Describes me very well

QUESTIONNAIRE

1. I daydream and fantasize, with some regularity, about things that might happen to me. (FS)
2. I often have tender, concerned feelings for people less fortunate than me. (EC)
3. I sometimes find it difficult to see things from the 'other guy's' point of view. (PT) (−)
4. Sometimes I don't feel very sorry for other people when they are having problems. (EC) (−)
5. I really get involved with the feelings of the characters in a novel. (FS)
6. In emergency situations, I feel apprehensive and ill-at-ease. (PD)
7. I am usually objective when I watch a movie or play, and I don't often get completely caught up in it. (FS) (−)
8. I try to look at everybody's side of a disagreement before I make a decision. (PT)
9. When I see someone being taken advantage of, I feel kind of protective toward them. (EC)
10. I sometimes feel helpless when I am in the middle of a very emotional situation. (PD)
11. I sometimes try to understand my friends better by imagining how things look from their perspective. (PT)
12. Becoming extremely involved in a good book or movie is somewhat rare for me. (FS) (−)
13. When I see someone get hurt, I tend to remain calm. (PD) (−)
14. Other people's misfortunes do not usually disturb me a great deal. (EC) (−)
15. If I'm sure I'm right about something, I don't waste much time listening to other people's arguments. (PT) (−)

16. After seeing a play or movie, I have felt as though I were one of the characters. (FS)
17. Being in a tense emotional situation scares me. (PD)
18. When I see someone being treated unfairly, I sometimes don't feel very much pity for them. (EC) (−)
19. I am usually pretty effective in dealing with emergencies. (PD) (−)
20. I am often quite touched by things that I see happen. (EC)
21. I believe that there are two sides to every question and try to look at them both. (PT)
22. I would describe myself as a pretty soft-hearted person. (EC)
23. When I watch a good movie, I can very easily put myself in the place of a leading character. (FS)
24. I tend to lose control during emergencies. (PD)
25. When I'm upset at someone, I usually try to "put myself in his shoes" for a while. (PT)
26. When I am reading an interesting story or novel, I imagine how I would feel if the events in the story were happening to me. (FS)
27. When I see someone who badly needs help in an emergency, I go to pieces. (PD)
28. Before criticizing somebody, I try to imagine how I would feel if I were in their place. (PT)

Now, to score your test, you will need to transform your responses into numbers. Next to each item you can see two letters in capitals between brackets. They indicate the subscale to which this particular item belongs.

PT = Perspective Taking scale
FS = Fantasy scale
EC = Empathic Concern scale
PD = Personal Distress scale

The minus sign that is found between brackets after some of the items indicates that the item should be scored in reverse order. So you need to use two different scoring schemes depending on whether the item has the (−) or not:

Without -: A=0, B=1, C=2, D=3, E=4
With -: A=4, B=3, C=2, D=1, E=0

You can then calculate your subscore for each scale by adding together the numbers you obtain from converting your answers to all items of a particular scale. For instance, for Perspective Taking you add the score of Items 3, 8, 11, 15, 21, 25, and 28, being careful to use the inverted rating for items 3 and 15. Your score for Perspective Taking can then range between 0 and 28, where 28 indicates that you report engaging very strongly and frequently in Perspective Taking, and 0 indicates that you do so very weakly and rarely. Then do the same for the other three scales.

You now have your score for each of the four scales. These scales measure complementary aspects of the way in which you react to other individuals. The Perspective Taking scale assesses your tendency to spontaneously adopt the psychological point-of-view of other individuals. The Fantasy scale taps into your tendencies to transpose yourself imaginatively into the feelings and actions of fictitious characters in books, movies, and plays. The other two subscales measure typical emotional reactions. The Empathic Concern scale assesses your "other-oriented" feelings of sympathy and concern for unfortunate others whereas the Personal Distress scale measures "self-oriented" feelings of personal anxiety and unease in tense, interpersonal settings.

On average, women have higher scores on all three subscales. A sample of over five hundred male and female college students indicated the following average scores[14]: for female students, FS=18.75, PT=17.96, EC=21.67, PD=12.28, for male students: FS=15.73, PT=16.78, EC=19.04, PD=9.46. If your scores were higher than the average for your sex, you are relatively empathic, if your scores were lower, you are relatively less empathic on that particular subscale of the questionnaire.